Riding
The Wild Orb

Roger L. Jewell

Published by:
Jewell Histories
Fairfield, PA

First Edition
2001

Printed
In the United States of America

ISBN # 0-9678413-1-3

Library of Congress Catalog Card Number, (not available)

To Order contact:

Jewell Histories
79 Ski Run Trail
Fairfield, PA.
17320

Phone (717)- 642-8342

Acknowledgments

First, I want to thank my friend who so graciously channeled my spirit guide whom I call Mr. "B." I also want to express my thanks to this loving guide for providing the primary message in this work.

I wish to thank those who read and critiqued the first drafts. Their diligent work has made this final book much more readable.

I wish to thank the three people who worked so hard on editing this final draft. This was not an easy task due to the nature of the work.

I also wish to thank those authors who have preceded me in this study of earth changes. They have broken the ground in a scientific investigation on the very edge of human experience.

Thank you,

Roger L. Jewell

Foreword

Even if you haven't read Roger Jewell's first book, "*Ancient Mines of Kitchi-Gummi,*" this second book is certainly a "must read" for anyone who has sought for answers to some of life's most important unresolved questions or a deeper meaning in their life.

Buckminster Fuller, America's Leonardo Da Vinci of the last century, foresaw a time in human history where an electronic network like the Internet would give humanity instant access to the combined knowledge of humankind and a clearer portrait of the universe. We are now living these times. His life-long preoccupation, with intuition and its capacity to co-relate life's experiences into coherent workable solutions to everyday problems, gives us an important reference point for accelerating our personal growth in this century.

Roger Jewell and his book are an important part of this synergetic stew "Bucky" envisioned for us. In it he has a unique way of weaving together the ideas of other authors and researchers. This functions like a catalyst, pushing our minds and hearts to a higher plateau of understanding. Like Bucky, who had tremendous respect for the potential of "regular people" to contribute to the resolution of the major problems of the twenty-first century, Roger gives us the confidence to proceed despite the old line that "Amateurs have no business putting their noses into the realm of the professionals."

Roger and myself share a love of Michigan's Northern Peninsula where he made a career of protecting its forests. We also have in common a profound respect for its history and residents. Lumbermen, fishermen and miners, whose acquired wisdom is invaluable to researchers from our urban universities.

Whether or not you consider channeling to be communications from other dimensions, our intuition at work (or simply gut-feelings), is unimportant. What is important is that we learn to screen and filter all sources of information and develop levels of discernment that will not exclude any sources of insight. As modern quantum physics along with ever more powerful microscopes reveal the dynamics of how our universe operates, we are inevitably being carried into a new way of looking at ourselves as "energetical beings." Like young birds learning to fly, we are a bit wobbly on our first flights, yet gaining strength and confidence as we experience this more subtle level of perception.

The saga of Roger's search for a new way of understanding the origins of massive forest fires on the planet is great reading. It will certainly give the reader new insights as well as a heightened confidence that all of us have the capacity to find the answers to major unresolved questions lingering within us.

Peter Kettenbeil

Peter is a Canadian writer, environmental technologist and life-long student and lecturer on the works of Buckminster Fuller.

Introduction

The following is a true story. It is a about a teacher I call Mr. "B," who through direct and channeled means, has helped me document an amazing lesson for mankind. It is in part, a theory about Earth weather, both short and long term, but it goes deeper into the essential nature of this magnetic third dimension. It touches on mankind's journey through time as we know it, and beyond, to some aspects we have failed to comprehend.

I called this lesson, *Riding the Wild Orb*, for the following reasons. The "ride," of course, is the journey of life itself in each physical lifetime. "Wild" is like wilderness, which for me represents a deep unknown expanse. Something I am part of, but, which for the most part, is well beyond my understanding. And "Orb," of course, because my world is round (a ball) like the sun God Baal of old, or like the ancient circle of life.

The book starts with my curiosity as a Minnesota farm boy. Then as a professional forester trying to understand the complex concepts of wild land fires, and what causes them. Finally, as a middle-aged man, I tried to figure out this thing called life and how to find my path and contribute. I had worked on part one for many years. Then abruptly, three years ago my life changed. I was given a teacher to expand my thinking and guide me in order to develop this story. The process went something like this:

I would study and develop a theory based on the information I had accumulated to that point. Then I would develop a set of questions and conduct a taped interview with Mr. "B." This was done through my friend who is a subconscious channel. These were private sessions that lasted about 30 minutes each. The book contains information from 26 of these sessions.

Several natural parts started to develop. The first part was the weather cycles I had been studying for so long. Next, I discovered how these cycles related to past cultures. Then, it expanded to include the predicted earth changes and, finally, how mankind fits into it all.

If you are like me, some parts will at first be hard to understand. Do not become discouraged. Move past the difficult section to what next catches your eye. You will eventually have to move back and forth between the four parts. They are all related, even if at first it doesn't seem so. I have had three years to try to digest it, so go easy on your self. I cannot simplify it. In fact, I have done my best to quote Mr. "B's" words directly. The book will tell one person one thing and the next person something else. This is how it should be. The book should not frighten you, and if it does, put it down for a while.

There is much mankind needs to know. The problem is getting the information to the right people. You can help here. If you read a part that is hard to understand but you think a friend might enjoy it, pass the book around. The people that are the least likely to pick this book up might need to read it the most, such as astronomers, weather specialists, healers, farmers, government scientists, etc. As you read it, I think you will understand why.

For me, this is part of my spiritual task. I have been blessed to receive this type of assistance. Mr. "B" was once a man like myself, but one who has gained enlightenment thousands of years ago. Now he is reaching back across the dimensions, or curtains if you will, to assist those of us who are still struggling on this side. A generous woman, who has allows him to speak through her body, does this channeling. She does not remember the message being transmitted when the session is completed. She desires to remain anonymous. She has gone public in the past, but soon her life was not her own. Please respect that.

As I struggle to make sense of this teaching, he provides guidance and answers to my questions. Not direction, but guidance. My free will is always expressed, and for that reason, this work is no doubt flawed in some ways. Regardless of these problems, I hope you will find the book interesting and challenging.

The one key point in the book is the phenomena called by some, *Earth Changes*. I prefer to think of this as just a normal part of this beautiful complex universe we live in. But, it is a part that we must grow to understand if we are to fully benefit from this experiencing place we call earth. I have put this into the scientific niche of weather, for that is what it is. But it is weather of a sort that we as mankind have not experienced for many millennia.

Finally, we look at ourselves, humanity, over this immense time and space. What are we really, and how do we relate to this creation? In the end we integrate all of these concepts into the hologram that they are. The intent is to achieve love and understanding at all levels of our beings. And, of course, to love the one creation of which we are all part. Everyone affects the hologram in a different way. But we all are important and have a niche to fill. The problem is to find it.

Table of Contents

Part 1 - Dramatic Weather Conditions

Part 2 - Cataclysmic Weather

Part 3 - Proof of Very Ancient Cultures

Part 4 - Humanities Roll

Graphics List

Tables

1 Planetary Weather Influences

Original Curiosity

My first interest in weather cycles goes back to the early sixties, when I worked for the US Forest Service. I lived in Mio, Michigan. As a young forester, I was able to take part in the suppression of many fires. This district had a history of several large, severe wild fires. The concept of dangerous fire weather became very familiar to me. It was an excellent training ground for new foresters.

One of our jobs was to record the weather. This entailed determining the humidity, the wind and a few other items needed to calculate the potential for serious fires. As I did this, my mind would run back to my forest fire history classes and the studies we had made of the fatal fires of 1871 and 1894, the Pestigo and Hinkley fires, respectively. These fires occurred in the area where I was born and raised. When I was young, it was hard to conceive fires that could burn whole towns, but by the sixties, I was well aware of the concepts, where deep fuel and dangerous weather can combine for disaster.

What were these cycles? Could they come back? The old fire fighters said, "Yes, they not only could, but they would, about every twenty years." As the years passed, and my fire experience increased, I knew they were right. The bad fires, of the late fifties and early sixties, made that point. Following that, the next decade was generally cooler. It started to heat up again in the eighties. By then I knew it wasn't simple. For example, what had caused the bad fires of 1972? As the data began to accumulate in my head, I quietly started looking for answers. By the mid-eighties, I was studying everything I could find that produced a weather cycle.

The first real information, I had known for years. It came from something my father said when we lived on our farm up in Pine County Minnesota. He told me on one August full moon, "If we get through tonight without the corn freezing, I think we will have until the full moon in September to get it chopped and in the silo." I asked, "Why, Dad?" He said, "Well it's always clear and coldest on the full moon." I just accepted it then without needing to know more.

The second piece of information came from a friend back in the sixties. We were planting some potatoes in his garden. He said, "I want to get them in tonight, because it is the dark of the moon." I just smiled and thought, this must be another old wives tale from New England.

My third piece of information came when I was reading a book on the Mayans and their famous calendar. I learned they had a name for the moon. They called it, "Storm Bringer." These three pieces of information came at intervals of 10 or 15 years. It was interspersed with my career in the U.S. Forest Service as a professional forester.

During this career, as outlined above, I was trained in the job of wild land fire prevention and suppression. One of my responsibilities was to protect the ranger district and the surrounding private lands from wild fire. As I tried to figure out the weather cycles, it became necessary to be a good observer. Studying the daily and seasonal weather was a very significant part of this work. Nothing made either my crew or my boss more disgusted than having to sit around waiting for fires in the rain, or having a bad fire start with only two people on duty. Now, you might ask, "What does this have to do with the project at hand?" The rest of this book will explain that.

By now I was looking to the planets for a possible cycle. If the ancients tracked the planets maybe they were involved. These bad fire years seemed to follow about a twenty-year cycle. Jupiter goes around every 12 years and Saturn goes around every 30 years. Where was the 20-year cycle? I put together a little spreadsheet early in my Mayan calendar studies. It was the first cycle of approximately 20 years.

Discovering the cycles of planet

I prepared a chart (graphic no. 1) that recorded the locations of Earth, Venus, and Jupiter. I was trying at the time to discover the cycles that may have been used by the ancient people. It was when I was working on my earlier book, *Ancient Mines of Kitchi-Gummi*. I made an assumption that at some point in time, these planets would be in one straight line out from the sun. From this imaginary point, I could rotate them and see what kind of pattern developed. This was strictly a model. I had no knowledge when this type of thing *might* happen.

The little one-page chart I was able to produce was a spectacular success. It indicated the location of each planet by the whole number of revolutions and the partial revolution to the fourth decimal point. I had set up formulas of movement for each planet. Then, by having days multiplied by the rate of movement in degrees per day, I would get the total number of degrees each planet would move. I divided the degrees by 360 to take out the whole cycles. The result was the partial cycle to four decimals. This translated into the location in degrees, e.g., .7500 of a circle = 270.

I had the spreadsheet print every 583 Days—the length of a conjunction between Venus and Earth. The results were immediate and fantastic. When starting from zero degrees, with all three of the planets in a line, it took exactly 20.75 years for them to line up again. This happened every thirteen Venus conjunctions.

The most amazing thing however, was unexpected. They lined up on the four primary Earth year marking points—fall equinox, summer solstice, spring equinox, winter solstice, then back to zero at the fall equinox. This is where I had started them in the first place. I got so excited with the cycles that I forgot the weather research and I began studying the Mayan calendar. This very simple chart had given a deep insight into how the calendar was structured.

I learned something else. The Mayan calendar has a glyph for the dates when Venus and Jupiter line up on the Earth marks, the two solstice dates and the two equinox dates. One writer had asked the question, why on these sacred Mayan calendar glyphs that mark the ends of each set of the thirteen Venus conjunctions, were there also season symbols? Even more puzzling, the progression of these symbols on the sacred Mayan calendar is counterclockwise. In Native American tradition, we usually see a clockwise progression of Spring, Summer, Fall and Winter.

Here, I inadvertently discovered an answer. The 20.75-year cycle was three months or one quarter of a year short. This caused the event to move backwards or counterclockwise on the circle of life. The reason they used this season mark was quite simple. Jupiter was the fourth object used on the calendar. It completed its cycle in eighty-three years, fifty-two Venus conjunctions. I knew the Mayan culture used the twenty moons repeated through thirteen Venus conjunctions as the basic 260-unit system. These conjunctions were measured against the Earth year's four-division base. I also assumed that these cycles terminated on some visual event. The logic then of the three solar bodies, (the moon, Venus, and Jupiter) in harmony with Earth could not be missed.

I have included this single page spreadsheet that describes this cycle. I bring it up here to clarify my description. It is a key to understanding the Mayan calendar and the general Earth planetary relationships.

Original Chart

| | COMPAIRSON LOC | | | |
VEN LOC	JUP DEG	JUP LOC	EAR DEG	EAR LOC
2.596119405	48.446134	0.1345725944	574.60299	1.5961194
5.19223881	96.892268	0.2691451889	1149.206	3.1922388
7.788358215	145.338402	0.4037177833	1723.809	4.7883583
10.38447762	193.784536	0.5382903778	2298.412	6.3844777
12.980597025	242.23067	0.6728629722	2873.015	7.9805971
15.57671643	290.676804	0.8074355667	3447.618	9.5767165
18.172835835	339.122938	0.9420081611	4022.2209	11.172836
20.76895524	387.569072	1.0765807556	4596.8239	12.768955
23.365074645	436.015206	1.21115335	5171.4269	14.365075
25.96119405	484.46134	1.3457259444	5746.0299	15.961194
28.557313455	532.907474	1.4802985389	6320.6329	17.557314
31.15343286	581.353608	1.6148711333	6895.2359	19.153433
33.749552265	629.799742	1.7494437278	7469.8389	20.749553
36.34567167	678.245876	1.8840163222	8044.4419	22.345672
38.941791075	726.69201	2.0185889167	8619.0449	23.941791
41.53791048	775.138144	2.1531615111	9193.6479	25.537911
44.134029885	823.584278	2.2877341056	9768.2509	27.13403
46.73014929	872.030412	2.4223067	10342.854	28.73015
49.326268695	920.476546	2.5568792944	10917.457	30.326269
51.9223881	968.92268	2.6914518889	11492.06	31.922388
54.518507505	1017.368814	2.8260244833	12066.663	33.518508
57.11462691	1065.814948	2.9605970778	12641.266	35.114627
59.710746315	1114.261082	3.0951696722	13215.869	36.710747
62.30686572	1162.707216	3.2297422667	13790.472	38.306866
64.902985125	1211.15335	3.3643148611	14365.075	39.902986
67.49910453	1259.599484	3.4988874556	14939.678	41.499105
70.095223935	1308.045618	3.63346005	15514.281	43.095224
72.69134334	1356.491752	3.7680326444	16088.884	44.691344
75.287462745	1404.937886	3.9026052389	16663.487	46.287463
77.88358215	1453.38402	4.0371778333	17238.09	47.883583
80.479701555	1501.830154	4.1717504278	17812.693	49.479702
83.07582096	1550.276288	4.3063230222	18387.296	51.075822
85.671940365	1598.722422	4.4408956167	18961.899	52.671941
88.26805977	1647.168556	4.5754682111	19536.502	54.26806
90.864179175	1695.61469	4.7100408056	20111.105	55.86418
93.46029858	1744.060824	4.8446134	20685.708	57.460299
96.056417985	1792.506958	4.9791859944	21260.311	59.056419
98.65253739	1840.953092	5.1137585889	21834.914	60.652538
101.2486568	1889.399226	5.2483311833	22409.517	62.248658
103.8447762	1937.84536	5.3829037778	22984.12	63.844777
105.44089561	1986.291494	5.5174763722	23558.723	65.440896
109.03701501	2034.737628	5.6520489667	24133.326	67.037016
111.63313442	2083.183762	5.7866215611	24707.929	68.633135
114.22925382	2131.629896	5.9211941556	25282.532	70.229255
116.82537323	2180.07603	6.05576675	25857.135	71.825374
119.42149263	2228.522164	6.1903393444	26431.738	73.421494
122.01761204	2276.968298	6.3249119389	27006.341	75.017613
124.61373144	2325.414432	6.4594845333	27580.944	76.613732
127.20985085	2373.860566	6.5940571278	28155.547	78.209852
129.80597025	2422.3067	6.7286297222	28730.15	79.805971
132.40208966	2470.752834	6.8632023167	29304.753	81.402091
134.99820906	2519.198968	6.9977749111	29879.356	82.99821

Graphic No. 1, Location Earth, Jupiter, and Venus.

The Mayan Clock

The evening sky, showing two bright planets along with the new moon on the spring or fall equinox, had to be a momentous occasion. I had discovered for myself, this ancient Mayan clock almost by accident, but I did not know how to put it in our time context. It was only by luck that it was approaching June 21, 1991 when I got to this point. The Forest Service Visitor Information Officer was having a summer solstice story-telling program at Pt. Iroquois Lighthouse. These were held on the beautiful sandy beach of Lake Superior. As Ranger I decided to attend. When the storytelling ended, we turned to gaze at the early evening moonlight. To my amazement, right before my eyes was the new sliver of a moon, Venus, and Jupiter. Nestled as close as they had been for 20.75 years. **The clock was started.** After summer comes spring, and 20.75 years from that day is March 21st, 2012—the date everyone is talking about. Again, there are more beautiful insights, but what of the weather?

I thought I had it, 20.75 years was close to the 20-year fire cycle. That would have been a good reason for the Ancients to watch and record everything as closely as they did. But, as I tried to correlate the dates to the fires I knew, nothing really seemed to fit. It was a while before I realized, having the calendar meant nothing, unless you know when things happened on it. (If one does not know that Valentine's Day is February 14, having a calendar will not keep you out of trouble with your wife).

I stumbled here for some time, trying to make data fit where it did not really belong. Then I gave up and started over with a whole new concept. Venus could not be part of the twenty-year fire cycle. Its effects may promote or detract on individual situations, but its cycles were too short to be part of the long-term constant. The Venus conjunctions come around every 1.6 years, five times every eight years. This might make one day's conditions worse, but it could not be the big player I was looking for.

I needed to look further out, perhaps to Saturn. What was the location of Saturn on those bad fire years? What was the conjunction cycle for Jupiter and Saturn? If in 12 years, Jupiter went once around the Sun and Saturn went about one third of the way, it would still take a few years to catch it again. In reality, the conjunction cycles turned out to be about 19.85 years. Now we had something—the conjunctions of both these large planets. Considering the effects would start before the actual conjunction and go beyond it some, we have an approximate cycle of 20 years. Not only do we have our cycle, but we have a possible cause for moisture loss on the larger continental bodies. If these solar bodies act as a full moon, we could have increased transpiration, caused by clear skies. This might even result in less moisture coming down when we get away from the ocean bodies.

These early assumptions I found to be based on inadequate data. As I soon discovered, the radiation also warms up the oceans and larger bodies of water causing wholly different weather situations. Although some fit was achieved, it seemed the drying effect of Jupiter over Earth summers might be more important than both Jupiter and Saturn over some other month. I might have given up if not for limited success in understanding some situations. This might be the cycle, but the problem was far more complex than I had assumed.

When these 19.85-year conjunctions fell over the Earth Summer, we had some of our most serious fire seasons. Although these cycles were not precisely 20 years, and the cycles are extremely long, I believed, at last, I had something. The problem is, a man's fire career only covers one or two cycles, and so answers must come from the records, not personal experience.

Reality A & B, what are they?

I need to identify just what I was talking about here. Did I really have anything? Could the twenty-year cycles, with the conjunctions of Jupiter and Saturn, be the real cause of extreme fire weather. What was actually happening? Maybe the weather seems to be warm and dry, but what could be the reason.

I need to identify several realities that I had no words for. I decided to use the old mathematical process and just indicate them by letters. First is Reality A. This can be defined as the state of the atmosphere around the Earth during a full moon. Up on our Minnesota farm, on an "August night", that would be "clear and cold." Some attributes of Reality A are, most likely, high pressure, a stable air mass (little wind) and, at night, substantial heat loss through radiation.

The next term we need to describe is Reality B. This can best be explained as the state of the atmosphere around Earth during the dark of the moon. Its attributes are likely to be warmer than normal, a higher probability of clouds, more air movement, and an increase in low pressure. This may result in more frequent and more intense storms.

As you can readily see, I have just defined the conditions people have observed during the full moon (Reality A) and the new moon, (Reality B). The premise I had developed at the beginning from my childhood information. To start with, these two realities just need to be accepted as possibilities.

To go on from here, I developed a theory. If the full moon caused Reality A, what would happen if some other heavenly body also was on the opposite side of Earth from the sun, for example, exterior conjunctions with Jupiter, Saturn or Mars? Would they also cause Reality A, intensify it, or what?

The second theory was, of course, if the new moon caused Reality B in Earth's atmosphere, could another solar body do the same thing? If Venus came between the Earth and the Sun as in an interior conjunction, would this also cause a Reality B situation in the Earth's atmosphere?

To test these theories I need actual data on the locations of these planets with regard to the Earth and Sun. Before I had a computer, I went to a local college library and secured photocopies of the pages that showed the internal conjunctions of Venus. This, of course, was just a date every 1.6 years. It did little to answer my questions. I would have to somehow get weather records to verify these findings. Were these dates actually warmer and more moist than average?

Here my project bogged down. There was too much lag-time between the dates and weather records that I had. However, in general, there seemed to be a relationship. Nothing I could prove, but a nagging sort of truth in the presumption that a conjunction with Venus would cause a Reality B, a warming of the Earth's atmospheric envelope.

As I was trying to expand my cycle of conjunction dates (I had only 3 or 4), I prepared a flat map of the solar system. By this time, I had learned the term "heliocentric," the location of the planets with the sun as a center reference point. It was here I discovered two basic pieces of information.

First, most work with planets is "geocentric," the solar system as seen from Earth. This helped me to see why no one was ever putting down the information I needed. We still had too much thinking of our Earth as the center of the universe. However, heliocentric data was available, and I was soon drawing circles around the Sun on pieces of paper. I needed to determine how these heliocentric numbers could be plotted.

Heliocentric Orientations of Planets

I soon realized the heliocentric data was similar to my forester compass that reads in azimuths. In other words, the space is divided up in 360 degrees, only backwards. It took me a little while to discover that the azimuth appeared to be a rough estimate of the 365-day year. Each day is about one degree. Fall equinox is about September 21. This is day 1 or 1 degree, and September 20, the next year is day 365 or azimuth 360 degrees.

When this is drawn as if you are looking at it from the top or the sun's north pole it appears to move backwards. My little charts looked sort of like this:

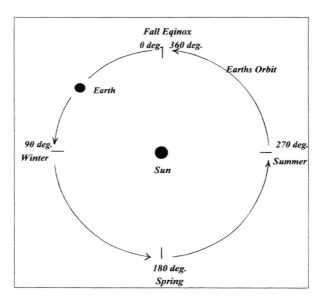

Graphic No. 2, Earth Rotation Around The Sun

Venus, The Five-Pointed Star, Reality B

I began plotting the conjunctions with Venus, just to discover the pattern. A most amazing thing happened. This was something I had never heard of. In fact, I have not known anyone who had heard of it. So, it may be newly re-discovered information, but most likely, my friends and I are just not too well read. But this is what I discovered.

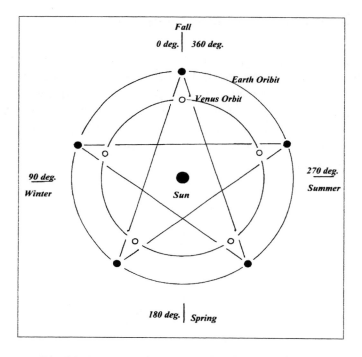

Graphic No. 3, Five-Star, Earth Venus Conjunction

Over a period of very close to 8 years there are five conjunctions with Earth and Venus. The most amazing thing I discovered is how when these five conjunctions are plotted, our five pointed star symbol comes into focus. The obvious conclusion is that the five-pointed symbol was used to represent a star, or more precisely, a planet.

There is another obvious assumption we can make. Anywhere in the distant past we find the five pointed star symbol in art or on pottery; we know they were already plotting the conjunctions of Venus. This introduces another question. Why?

11

Plotting the Conjunctions of Jupiter and Saturn

When we plot the conjunctions of Jupiter and Saturn in the same fashion we find the triangle. This triangle nearly repeats itself much as the star does. When these triangle points (conjunctions) fall on summer serious weather conditions can happen. So here we not only have our twenty-year fire cycle, but the more intense 60-year fire cycles of 1870s, 1930s and 1990s as well.

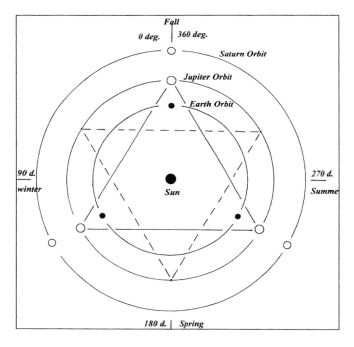

Graphic No. 4, Jupiter Saturn Conjunction Triangle

In real-time, I bought a computer here and got seriously derailed in studying planetary cycles and the Mayan calendar. But, I want you to just hold these two images while we get back to the weather issue.

Weather Effects

Using the newly found information on the cycle for Venus, I bet my boss that it would get up to 45 degrees F. in the Michigan Upper Peninsula on January 15, 1990, which was the next up-coming Venus conjunction. I had observed that the November conjunction, 3.2 years earlier, had caused a warm spell. I had been testing my theory for several years already. My computer was up and running with a Heliocentric Ephemeras on disc so exact planetary locations could be predicted.

Needless to say, that particular week in January of 1990, we did get to 45 degrees F. This led me to believe in one more of the old stories, the occasional "January Thaw." This term probably developed from the 8-year cycle of Venus and Earth conjunctions in mid-winter. I was elated and soon dug into my studies even harder. Of course, I still worked full-time, and carried on a normal life. There was no time for hours in front of the computer. But now back to the cause of these effects.

Cause of Reality A

If Reality B was working with Venus, causing warm weather, what about using the biggest planet out there, Jupiter, for Reality A? If anything should create Reality A, it should be Jupiter.

These early years Jupiter was located at Earth's 280 azimuth during the summer of 1984 and 310 azimuth in the summer of 1985. And yes, Reality A did appear for those months; we were between Jupiter and the sun. The air was still and the weather was sunny and warm—almost hot. This created beautiful days to go camping in the Forest Service campgrounds. It was so nice. In fact, I almost got the wrong idea.

I began to think that when we got between Jupiter and the sun, Reality A, the Earth's atmosphere was actually warmer. It was only luck that I was able to hear about the record breaking cold that July, in Australia. What was this? Then I remembered the Minnesota August nights on the farm with a full moon and high heat loss.

Of course, Australia was on the dark side of the Earth in July, so they were experiencing excessive heat loss. Of course, it was winter, so it was made worse by this effect. Now, I had something more to describe Reality A. If you were in summer during Reality A, there would be clear skies and a lot of sunshine. Maybe it would even be hot. But if you were in winter during Reality A, it could be extremely cold. Reality A must be a special situation where both hot and cold radiation is increased. The effect of it is increased and multiplied by the lack of air movement. This is one very important piece of information for the world's weather.

Cause of Reality B

You cannot think of Reality B space as a crossing like you can think of Reality A. It is more appropriate to think of it as two sisters meeting. "Gaia and Venus" are having a warm conversation in passing with a little blending of their energies, and some air movement developing around the affair. When Venus gets in between the Sun and Earth, she may cast a magnetic shadow on Earth or stir the magnetic soup as she spins by.

However, the effects of this should not be under-estimated; the result could be fatal. Reality B meetings must be thought of with regard to when and where they happen. Just like the Indian summer of November 1986, all enjoyed the friendly meeting in January 19 of 1990. Most also enjoyed the warm snow-less winter of 1998 in my Gettysburg, Pennsylvania area. The hot summer visit during 1996, when Gaia's big uncle Jupiter was heating up the north equatorial current of the North Atlantic with a Reality A, was not pleasant. When Gaia's solar brothers and sister all visit simultaneously, things can get out of hand. Just like with our own family get together, it is often too much, in too short a time. When this happened in 1996 the resulting hurricane season was disastrous. It could have been even more deadly if luck had not pushed two of the worst storms out to sea.

Now that I had the theories, it became necessary to understand and finally prove them.

Several years later I did check this out with my spirit guide, Mr. "B," who is being channeled by a friend.

R: "Is it true that, the Earth gets physically warmer during its conjunction with Venus?" *B: "Yes."*

R: "Did the ancients know this?" *B: "Yes."*

R: "Is the current warm weather, 1/5/98, a direct temperature increase resulting from the conjunction with Venus?" *B: "Yes."*

R: "Is the air pressure lower?" *B: "Yes."*

R: "Is it true that, when Earth conjuncts with Jupiter, there is a general higher air pressure, and both incoming and outgoing radiation is increased?" *B: "Yes, that is correct. It is also when you have greater turbulence on Earth."* R: "Like Earthquakes and such?" *B: "Yes."*

15

2   Effects of Reality A & B

I believed it was just going to be a matter of time before I had nice clear definitive proof of these two concepts. This assumption was a product of both arrogance and ignorance. Smarter men than me had been trying to prove what caused the fire cycles for years. They also came up with more possibilities than proven facts. The complexities of weather are enormous on a world scale. It depends not only on the solar radiation but where and when does this heat strike. Is it on the ocean surface or on the land, northern hemisphere or southern, etc.? What effects do the wind currents or ocean currents have on the excess heat or excess heat loss?

Regardless, some constants did exist and there must be a way to prove them. Since this is not a book about facts, but instead, possibilities and theory, the whole purpose is to tell others what I have perceived. When enough perceptions are put together, maybe some facts will follow. I then started to record what I did know.

Although it is difficult to find hard data to prove these theories, I will tell you what I did find. For example, in Reality B, I personally noticed several interesting weather phenomena. First, there was the warm Indian summer weather in Sault Ste. Marie, Michigan, mentioned earlier. This happened during the 11/8/86 Venus conjunction. We also had a beautiful fall in 1994 in Gettysburg, PA, thanks to the 11/4/94 conjunction. A few years earlier when I was still at the Sault, I observed the thaw of January 19, 1990. The recent winter here at Gettysburg, PA, 97-98, we all enjoyed the winter that never happened. I believe this was because of the January 15, 1998, Venus conjunction, that was exactly eight years later than the one in the Sault. I have come to believe this has happened enough over the last hundreds of years to spawn the two terms we all have heard, "January Thaw" & "Indian Summer."

Even though I only have limited scientific evidence, I believe someday we will have proof of this Venus effect. This will happen when we have learned how to screen out some of the other weather noise and measure these eight-year Venus cycles. It's my personal belief the ancients knew this, and that was one of the reasons Ishtar (Venus) was thought to be able to raise or quiet the storms.

I also believe the facts prove that we can expect serious weather anomalies in the Northern Hemisphere if we have a Venus conjunction and a Jupiter conjunction close together and within a few weeks of the summer solstice. This can probably be on either side of the twenty-first, as happened in June of 1948, 1972 and 1996.

Reality B and A Together

As an example of this, I was able to predict the serious weather for the summer of 1996. I didn't guess the greatness of the Mississippi River floods. I did know, however, when Reality B weather with its low pressure and winds, connected with the Reality A weather just 20 days later, and when the sun was near its northern maximum, there would be serious weather events in the Northern Hemisphere. I was not disappointed.

I was also able to relate the very significant weather events of June 1972 (Hurricane Agnes) to the drastic floods of the Mississippi River Valley in 1996. In effect, the joint visits of Venus on the inside making it warm and windy and with Jupiter on the outside with its special radiation, match perfectly with the weather extremes. Jupiter's heating up the Atlantic just north of the equator, creates hurricane conditions. Add this to Venus's increasing temperature, extreme low-pressure storm cells and increasing wind, and you have conditions for extreme weather.

One last, but major point of Reality B is when Venus warms up the air envelope around Earth it increases the capacity of that air envelope to hold moisture. As this increased moisture is being stored it does not come down as rain. This causes a drought or reduction in the rain before the conjunction. As Venus passes it no longer is increasing the heat-related moisture storage capacity of Earth's air envelope. The moisture begins to fall. As Venus starts to move away, after the conjunction, the air actually begins to cool. This causes above average rainfall. This was perfectly exhibited before and after the August 21, 1999 conjunction in the southeastern USA.

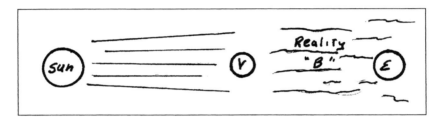

Graphic No. 5, Sketch of Reality B

It doesn't end here. The super-heated air holds extra moisture that eventually comes down as snow the following winter. This above-average snowfall has a lot of moisture content. When it melts the following spring, we get floods like the ones in April of 1973, the highest flood levels since 1844. Again, in early 1997, melting from heavy snows caused record damage in the upper Mississippi river valley.

The records from the summer of 1948, the winter of 48/49, and the flood stages of April 1949 should tell a similar story.

Enough said about Reality B. Now, what can I say about that special place in the sky we call Reality A.

Reality A

First let me talk about Super Reality A events. This is when both Jupiter and Saturn are in conjunction. This happens about every twenty years, and the event turns through Earth's year about 120 degrees each time. This means if one event falls on the June Summer Solstice it will return to near that date 60 years later. Now, we know Saturn moves only about 12 degrees a year and Jupiter only about 30 degrees, therefore this event will be significant for about three successive years. The slowness of Saturn's rotation will stretch it out even more if the conditions are right.

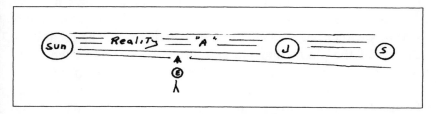

Graphic No. 6, Sketch of Super Reality A

Reality A is best expressed in drought and fire weather. Therefore I will outline the effects in the context of past fire weather I have experienced or am familiar with.

I believe, the severe fire cycles, that are generally about twenty years, but sometimes are more extreme on the sixty-year cycles, are caused by these phenomena. The 1870s and 1880s, the 1930s and 1940s, and the 1980s and 1990s, these were all representative of the Jupiter Saturn conjunctions that occurred in the general summer period. All three of these periods on the sixty-year cycle exhibited extreme weather phenomena in the central and western U.S. This was especially true from just east of the divide to the west edge of the Mississippi River Basin. In the Mississippi River Basin the

Gulf of Mexico supplies water to offset the additional heat and modifies the condition.

The first period started with the great Pestigo and Chicago fires of October 1871. This resulted in from 1200 to 2000 people killed and hundreds of thousands acres burned. At the same time, serious fires of the pinelands of Michigan destroyed thousands more acres of forests.

The second serious event we are aware of is known as the Dust Bowl of the thirties. This Reality A effect, caused by conjunction of Jupiter and Saturn in late 1921, is legendary. Even if the cause was not recognized. The slow movement of Jupiter and Saturn through the summer skies of the twenties and thirties caused one of the worst droughts in this nation's history. This is where a combination of man's lack of knowledge, and a severe weather pattern came together in disaster. The great dust storms of the plains and the extreme fire seasons of the mid-west forests brought our economic system to its knees. The drought forced the abandonment of millions of acres of small farms. The fires destroyed the young growth timber just getting started after the great cuts of earlier in the century. In general, very serious environmental damage was sustained due to humanities ignorance of the weather cycles.

The third event we can tie to the Jupiter Saturn conjunction in 1980. This took place in the skies over spring. Again, as in the thirties, the two planets moved in unison through the skies with resulting bad fire seasons one year after another. Many of you probably remember the Great Yellow Stone Fires of 1988 when man's no-burn fire policy clashed with a Jupiter/Saturn event. I will now use the actual fire experience to exhibit these events.

Fire Behavior as Proof

A good model would be helpful to put this together. However, I have re-created what I could using all the fire histories I was able to locate. I needed to go back to my years of fire observations for some hard evidence, real dates and real times. So, I gathered up the fire data and started to do an analysis. The results were slow, but patterns were developing. We will take one special type of weather at a time.

Eastern and Mid-Western Fire Effects in 1961

Now let's look at what happened in this Super Reality A that took place on April 16, 1961. The Jupiter and Saturn conjunction was positioned over 293 degrees or about July 15th in Earth's annual revolution around the sun. It is necessary to understand that when this conjunction takes place is not as important, as where it takes place in Earth's year.

The effects of this Jupiter/Saturn Conjunction started to take effect much earlier. For example, in 1958 Saturn was located over early June, and Jupiter was located over April 15, both in a very potent location for the Northern Hemisphere. In that year, Venus was also in conjunction with Earth in around February. This causes an early and warm spring. This brought on an early fire season potential in 1958.

By 1959, the early season heating caused by Jupiter and Saturn was getting worse. Venus was not yet having an effect, but when she does a little later in June and July, it only makes the problem more serious.

The spring fire season is always the worst in the Midwest. The jet stream brings in the dry Canadian air. If cloud cover or rain does not temper this, the sun's radiation quickly heats up the dry ground. The air mass warms up, but since no moisture is present, the relative humidity may quickly drop to the 15% range. This is the ideal situation to cause fire problems, and in 1959, these problems were very serious. One large fire on the Jack Pine Sand Plains of northwestern Wisconsin was especially bad that year. It burned 15 or 20 miles with about a mile-wide front. It jumped several roads and even a relatively large river. We forestry students from the University of Minnesota were given a special tour that we might experience this once-in-a-career happening.

By June of 1959, I was in Bly, Oregon, working on the Klamouth National Forest as part of their summer fire crew. I arrived about June 14 and got to take the weekend of June 21 off, but the rest of the summer I had to work every day. The fire weather was extreme for the rest of the summer until I left in August. The dust in the mountains was 4 to 6 inches deep on the forest roads and numerous serious fires burned.

The summer of 1960 and 1961 I was in the Navy and do not remember the fire conditions. For these years I want to quote Stephen Pyne from his book *Fire in America* on how the effects of the deepening Super Reality A were being acted out. It started in 1957 talking about a fire around Chatsworth, New Jersey.

> *Twenty thousand acres of the same area re-burned in 1954, and in 1957 fire swept some 54,000 acres and 50 structures in Plymouth City, Massachusetts. ... It was during the prolonged drought of 1961-1965 that the fire potential of the coastal plains drew national attention. Three fires on Long Island—one in 1962 and two in 1963 burned a total of 7,000 acres and consumed 200 structures. In the spring of 1963 conditions were severe. Massachusetts reported 4,861 fires in one month, though none became major. Fires moved out of the woods and into the suburbs around New York, and Philadelphia and in a wide region encompassing Pennsylvania, Maryland, West Virginia, Virginia, and Kentucky. Conditions were the worst since 1930.*
>
> *But it was in New Jersey that the real firestorm broke loose. On May 20, 1963, a series of fires began*

an 11-day rampage over more than 200,000 acres. Some 458 structures were destroyed, and seven lives lost and more than a thousand people left homeless. Pyne, (17) p. 63-64.

This is what can happen when a Super Reality A hits at the peak of summer in the Northern Hemisphere. This will happen again in the year 2020, making from 2017 - 2023 very dangerous years for both drought and fire in the East and Midwest. Sixty years of global warming will make the expected results even worse.

By 1964 I was again back on a fire district, the Mio District of the Huron-Manistee National Forest. Jupiter was passing out of the picture, but the built up effects of the long Saturn pass during summer were still evident. In that year Venus came by in mid-summer again (279 degrees). On the deep dry Jack Pine Sands of Mio the pre-conjunction drying plus the high winds of Venus caused several bad spring and early summer fires. I remember on one day I went on six of the eight fires that burned that day. Most were started because the high winds were blowing trees into the power lines. At the same time we had relative humidity around 12-15 %.

Jupiter and Venus, 1972, Reality A & B

By 1972, Jupiter was again making its presence known. During the summer of 1971 no Venus activity was taking place but Jupiter was located squarely over late May. This meant we had a lot of high radiation days. This had the effect of deep drying of the bug-killed spruce and fir trees in northwestern Minnesota. By deep drying, I mean the large stems of standing or fallen dead trees. Again in the spring of 1972, the sun's radiation was very warm. This was enhanced by the up-coming

Venus conjunction on June 20. In fact, on about June 20 both Jupiter and Venus were going to be in conjunction.

But for the fire effects we need to look just before the conjunctions, in this case May 15th, the first day of fishing season. As I said the spring was sunny and dry, and the local fire staff men on the Superior National Forest were trying to reduce the hazard by burning some cutover slash and brush areas. They were not totally aware how different this spring was from normal. The potential of strong winds whipped up by the approaching Venus conjunction, and the extreme radiation being caused by both Jupiter and Venus now near conjunction were not evident. In addition, the deep drying caused by last summer's clear days made the time ripe for a bad fire.

When their stubborn slash fire just did not want to burn out, only a few men were left to guard it on that first day of fishing season weekend. These men had not even gotten out to the fire yet when the morning wind had picked up and blew sparks over the line and with the extreme low humidity, new fires caught immediately. By the time the crew arrived the fire that was to be known as the Little Sioux Fire had escaped and was quickly building. Twenty thousand acres and several million dollars later, people had time to stop and think what went wrong. About the only thing they did not blame was Jupiter or Venus, the true instigators of the extreme conditions.

Jupiter/Saturn Conjunction of 1981 (189 degrees)

This Super Reality A was a near repeat of the 1920s and1930s. The conjunction happens as both Saturn and Jupiter are moving north across the equator. This allows time for one pass of Saturn and two passes of Jupiter in the Northern Hemisphere. The super radiation build-up stored heat reserves in the northern oceans and a long and dangerous set of serious fire weather conditions exist. On some years, conditions of heavy rain or severe storms co-exist in near-water locations.

Drought Indicators, 1983 & 1986 on the Hiawatha Forest

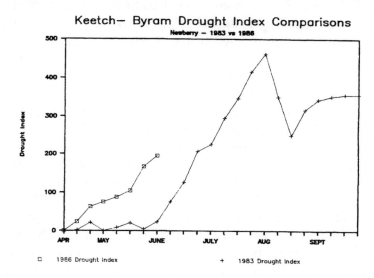

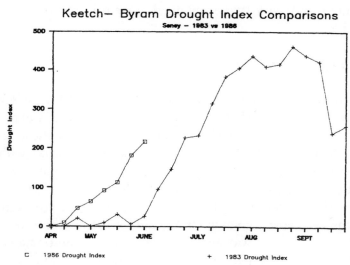

Graphic No 7
Drought Charts of Hiawatha National Forest

25

The 1983 drought index chart indicates a typical drought that is brought on by intensive radiation from Saturn at about May 1 and Jupiter over June 1 in Earth's solar year. With these preheating conditions, when the Venus conjunction started approaching about two and one half months before the late summer conjunction, the drought began in earnest. The super drying caused by the increasing heat of the air envelope did the trick. The drought broke within a week after the Venus conjunction passed. Jupiter hit mid-summer by 1984.

In 1986 Jupiter moved to the late summer location Venus had been in 1983. The heating caused by Saturn over June 1 and the increasing radiation of Jupiter now around August 31 also blocked the mid-summer rains in the area of the Hiawatha National Forest. This caused a second summer of drought similar to 1983, but with different underlying factors. This was a bad fire year in many places. By 1987 serious fires were again erupting, but because no Venus activity was available, lightning and wind were subdued. Control was difficult but possible.

The Yellow Stone Fires

Serious fires burned during the 1980s, but the most serious group occurred in what is now called the Yellow Stone fires. We need to look at the circumstances to see how these conditions developed. As I said these fire seasons started with the Super Reality A of 1981. Jupiter and Saturn came into conjunction on 186 degrees. This is March 27 in the Earth's year. Then, these two great planets moved through the summer months each year somewhat in unison for the next few years.

By 1988 Venus was again poised to be in conjunction with Earth on June 14 (263 degrees), but now the situation was becoming extreme. The last eight years of hot dry summers had dried the dead and down bug-killed and aging pine of the Yellow Stone area. Many of these dead trees had just succumbed to the recent drought and stood as sentinels ready to be struck by lightning. When Venus came through, no moisture was available to generate rain. All that came was dry lightning and wind. This along with the extreme dry fuel condition created the holocausts that followed.

Managers, thinking it would be good to let some of this dangerous fuel burn up, did not react until many of the fires were to big to handle. By fall, everyone from the President on down was looking for someone to blame, but to my knowledge, no one blamed the planets.

I think when it is all written down and checked out and when new models for fire activity based upon the location of these three great weather makers are made, people will realize Venus can truly make the fires from hell as an ancient Sumerian poem suggests.

Although it takes a careful study of the exact starting dates and weather build-up to see the direct relationships of these fires to the planet's locations, I believe the correlation is unmistakable.

El Nino

We also have other weather effects. As long as we are working on Reality A, let's move from fire to hurricanes and El Ninos. Many have been asking what causes El Nino. I believe I can demonstrate what this is, but first, I must introduce another term. We will call this the Pacific Counter Current Pool (PCCP).

By now, I am sure you have begun to picture Reality A as a place in the solar system that lies mostly between Jupiter and the sun. To a lesser degree it is also between Saturn and the sun. It is at its maximum between the sun and Jupiter and Saturn in conjunction. Now this space is not just anywhere out there. Its location can be thought of as some place in Earth's year. Remember the azimuth type reading we used in the helio-centric relationship with the sun or more simply, the days of the year. For the intense heat needed for fires, we use the summer period of the Northern Hemisphere, June, July, and August. We now switch to two new locations out there around the sun. We call these 0 and 180 degrees or more simply, the dates 9/20 and 3/20. The sun is directly over the equator. When the sun is directly overhead the radiated heat is at its peak. We could think of these two dates as the summer of all countries on the equator. Their winter, if you could call it that, is on the summer solstice and the winter solstice. This can be also thought of as the time when the Northern Hemisphere and the Southern Hemisphere both get an equal period of sunshine.

But to continue, remember the term we started with, PCCP. This pool is under the most direct rays of the sun as it passes through the Reality A zone in space on these two dates. There are two things we know about PCCP. It's big and it turns in on itself. It does not go out to the poles where it can cool off. On my globe, these currents appear to stay within a 20-degree lati-tude zone between 10S and 10N.

Herein lies the problem. The waters of the PCCP are super-heated by the unusual characteristics of the Solar radiation in Reality A space. This usually takes place within the two months closest to the fall equinox. A similar effect happens in the spring equinox but the result is different. The difference is in the Pacific Ocean north of the equator and south of the equator. It appears that the two currents called the counter current and the north equatorial current hold more water in the closed loop near the equator than does the southern equatorial current. This allows the warm temperature in the water to build up. There would also be residual heat stored in the northern Pacific in general from the Reality A effect during the previous few summers. In some years these effects are made worse by the quick heating of the atmosphere during the Venus conjunctions over summer.

This theory would then assume that you could get El Nino effects roughly twice every thirteen years based on Jupiter. The moving north effect would be greater than the effect moving south, at least for the Northern Hemisphere.

We must also realize the El Ninos cause by super Reality As, which are caused when Jupiter and Saturn are in conjunction, will always be much worse.

Heating in The Southern Hemisphere

There is a third Reality A effect I would like to discuss here. We must realize that if there is a Reality A effect during June and July crossing in the Northern Hemisphere, then there surely must be similar December and January crossing effects in the Southern Hemisphere. Well, this just came up in November and December of 2000. This period was a super Reality A because when it took place, Jupiter and Saturn were still near conjunction.

Due to delays in publication, draft copies of this book were written and copyrighted before the event (3/4/99). I am including quotes of what I predicted at that time concerning this event.

"There is one last thing I can say. These great weather machines do not stop. They continue to move and churn through the their sixty-year cycles out there in the space soup"... "This may or may not be important in the USA, but it will cause even more heat and drought in Australia. This one will fall in November of 2000. This conjunction may breed disaster for that region in both 1999 and 2000. The heat will be extreme and dangerous. Large inversion layers may add to the problems. The situation could be life threatening. Australian weather and agricultural communities should prepare for it as best they can. "

"The possibility of either disastrous storms or fires should

29

be expected in March of 2001 when Venus comes by. Which, storm or fire, will depend on the local weather patterns, and if water is available."

"This weather event is very significant. It will affect other parts of the world. <u>The interiors of the large Northern Hemisphere continents can expect extreme cold and dry those same months. There will probably be cold weather in Russia and Canada. Northern countries should secure extra heating fuel supplies</u>." (Emphasis added)

Although I have not been able to secure precipitation and drought records for 1999 and 2000 from Australia, there was a lot of news about heat in the Southern Hemisphere.

One important event did happen in Mozambique, Africa. Apparently the excess heat with adequate water from the ocean caused extensive record flooding.

There was no question of the cold in the Northern Hemisphere. Heating oil supplies were short and prices skyrocketed. In the North Eastern United States it was proclaimed to be the coldest winter for 105 years. I am sure Canada and Russia also had records. If only in March of 1999 I had taken my own advice and invested in oil futures.

The effect of Reality A must also be considered on what it does to ocean temperatures. When a Reality A event occurs on or below the equator, the ocean is the primary recipient of the super radiation. If this extra energy is comprised of ultra-violet radiation, it is absorbed by the ocean instead of being reflected. It will be transformed into heat energy in the oceans. This heat can slowly build up and trigger hurricanes, the El Ninos or other serious storm conditions.

Summary

I prepared a chart of the conjunctions of Earth and Venus along with the locations of Jupiter and Saturn on the same date. I had listed these for the sixty-year period for which I had some data. When I compared this to Dr. Glanz's chart of climatic anomalies, the correlation is quite noticeable. I believe when sophisticated weather modeling systems can compensate for heat storage by the oceans, even more will be learned.

Only now am I learning how complicated the whole process becomes. When the solar radiation falls on water instead of land, two very different results can happen. The solar radiation is absorbed by the oceans and circulated into other air currents. So water heated along the Atlantic Ocean equator can make hurricanes that move up into the temperate zones. Or, if the extra heated water is in the Pacific Counter-Current Pool, an El Nino can be born.

I have worked on this problem for over twenty years. I have discussed it with many foresters with always the same result. Interesting, but where do we go with it? I know now that I cannot prove all of the above statements, but I know they are substantially correct. It's now up to you, the reader. Some of you will have a slightly different knowledge base or a different perspective, and the answers, if we are diligent, will start coming.

By What Process Is This Caused?

In this part, we are going to speculate on the causal agents that might be involved in these, Reality A and Reality B zones. To begin with, I think it is now a well-established fact that the universe isn't an empty vacuum between the celestial bodies we know and see. There is something more out there. Some have speculated and others have even named what the material might be. However, in this book, we will just call it Space Soup.

We have all heard of the North Pole and the South Pole. Most of you have also heard of the Magnetic Pole. We sometimes visualize our planet as a bar magnet.

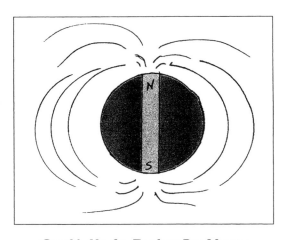

Graphic No. 8a, Earth as Bar Magnet

I am not sure if people know why the Earth has a magnetic field, but I have heard that sometime the current shifts. The north polarity becomes south, and the south polarity becomes north. *"The Magnetic Field reverses polarity. More than 170 polarity changes or field reversals have occurred during the past 80 million years. All this has been learned only in the past three decades, through study of paleomagnetism, the magnetism of rocks."* (5) p 9

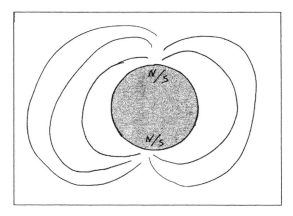

Graphic No. 8b, Earth as an Electromagnet

We know the Earth has an ample supply of iron in it. We also know that if iron is put into an electric field, it will pick up some of that electricity and create its own magnetic field. This principle is the basis for all electric motors, generators and electro-magnets.

Here, we go beyond the known and into the area of theory. If the Earth is not a bar magnet and yet has an electrical field, it could then be a mass of iron passing through an electrical field, which in turn generates the Earth's magnetic field. We also know that the Earth's magnetic field changes or fluctuates. Therefore, to continue our speculation, the electrical field that Earth is passing through must also fluctuate. Sometimes it may be negative, and at others times it may be positive. We can assume this is true if its structure is responsible for the occasional changing of our North Pole to a South Pole—magnetically speaking, that is.

It now appears, we could say that our Space Soup is charged and that these charges are not neatly uniform. Since the Sun and Jupiter are gravitationally attached and related, they may also be magnetically connected. If the Space Soup changes, we have something to put into Reality A crossings that could create the effects we are observing. Maybe, the Reality A crossing areas have a more strongly aligned magnetic field, and in some way this intensifies the radiation. This could provide additional heat when the modified radiation hits the Earth's surface. It could also cause a loss of heat on the dark side of the Earth. Not being a physicist, I will conclude this here.

To summarize part one of this book, let's take a second look. The planets, as well as the moon, can affect the weather. **First, they do this by creating something we have called Reality B meetings and Reality A crossings.**

Next, these special arrangements of the planets can and do have serious effects on the weather of North America, Australia and a place we call PCCP (the Pacific Counter

Current Pool) made up of the Counter Current—and the Northern Equatorial Current.

We have in a very limited way tried to prove these effects with hard data. Much more is needed before that can satisfactorily be done. I am convinced that the hard evidence exists. I just do not have the money or the time to prove it with the scientific method. Some proofs are expressed in Chapter 4.

Below are my discussions with Mr. "B" relevant to this chapter.

R: "Can you give me a hint about what I should do with the information about the planets and the weather?" *B: "As you continue to study and research, you are going to find more patterns, and by that I mean, more effects of other planets and galaxies, and their effect on this planet you call Earth. And, as you do research, you will be able to predict patterns in changes of this planet. That could be useful, although we don't know yet if it will be well-received, in preventing famines and starvation of large groups of people and disease, and as you do your research and your computations pay close attention, very close attention, to what occurs when huge meteorite showers are hurled toward your planet. These are important guideposts or signposts that something is about to occur. When you are aware this is occurring, look and see which planet has the most influence on this planet, and begin to chart your findings. Humanity is going to need more information than what they currently have if humanity is to survive in the future."*

R: "Is their any clue as to where I should go, from where I am now, on this weather question?" *B: "If you are very attentive and watch the current weather pattern, particularly in the region of Australia and New Zealand, and watch what occurs, you will have more than enough questions to do your research and find the proof you are endeavoring to find, and will have it in time to be effective before it occurs globally. That individuals listen, that remains to be seen. Some will."*

R: "Am I right in my assumption that much of the increased radiation heat is hidden in the latent heat of evaporation and, therefore, doesn't show up in the temperature?" *B: "That is correct."*

R: "It seemed like that was a problem. For years I struggled with average temperatures and couldn't find anything. Do the professional weather modelers use the planet locations in their weather models?" *B: "Most do not."*

R: "In this country would any of them do it?" *B: "Umm, very few, if any."*

R: "If I use this information, would it increase the accuracy of these models?" *B: "Oh, indeed."*

R: "Could you explain how that would be done?" *B: "It is a very complex process, but it would make them far, umm, what is the word? Not comprehensive, what is the word I am searching for? What is the word that collects data?"* (I was of no help.) *B: "What is that word?"* (Pause) R: "At least when they collect the data from within years certain things happen and feed it back into the computer that would . . . That's what it seems to me . . . how they should do it?" *B: "Yes, but what is that word? There is a word. It would make that a thousand times more accurate, if they would collect it in the sequence it should be collected, in the cycles."* R: "That's what I was thinking. If they developed a formula for the three basic cycles, Jupiter, Saturn, and Venus" . . . *B: "Correct."* R: . . . "Then re-create their model to those cycles." *B: "Then it would be much, much, much more accurate.* " R: "That's what I was thinking, but I wasn't sure."

R: "You once told me I would get information soon enough to avoid starvation and famine if people would listen. It seems to me the most serious threat of drought and famine in the Northern Hemisphere will be related to the super conjunction of Jupiter and Saturn, plus Earth and Venus around June 20, 2020. Is this correct?" *B: "Yes."*

R: "And the drought should start as early as 2015?" *B: "2012, 2015 and it depends on the tilt and the rotation of the Earth, you see."* R: "And it could run as long as 2023, I thought." *B: "It could, yes."*

R: "If people listen to the caution, what should they do?" *B: "If they listen, they will know what to do."* R: "OK." *B: "Because each region is going to be . . ."* (pause, broken sentence) *" . . . specific needs for that region. There are going to be some basic needs, but in higher elevations and more northern climates, their needs would be simply different than an arid hot climate, you see. But, if they listen they will know what to do."* R: "OK."

R: "Can the red shift information by T. Jaakkola (Ref.- 23) be used to explain why it is warmer when Venus gets between us and the sun?" (This is in reference to an astronomical process where light rays going around a solar body are bent by the magnetic factors they encounter) *B: "That is a partial explanation, but as I have explained to you earlier, it is more than known planetary involvement. It is galactic involvement. What occurs here on this planet occurs, or is the results of the galactic impact effects on all things. Not just this planet. Do you understand this I speak?* R: "I think so."

B: "Yes, you can't talk about one in reality without delving into the other because it's all related."

R: (I believe my follow-up question went like this. It is missing on the tape of the session. "So then the planets and The Earth Shift processes are related?" *B: "Indeed it is. What do you think affects the planetary movements? It is not some random scattering of objects in the atmosphere. There are things that move these planets, these asteroids, these moons, and these galaxies that we're speaking of."* This is as close as Mr. "B" gets to frustration with my inability to understand this complex subject.

R: "Is light enhanced, changed, or bent as it passes through a variable magnetic field?" *B: "Certainly."*

R: "How does that work?" *B: "Magnetic fields are charged particles, and charged particles will always have impact on light as it passes through them, it will bend it. If you had, let me break this down. If you yourself were a beam of light and all this furnishing in this room was charged particles of a magnetic field you couldn't randomly pass through this room from one side to another. You would have to make pathways, see?"* R: "Yes." *B: "That is what a magnetic field does to light, it has to bend its pathway. Do you understand the correlation I am endeavoring to make?"*

3   What Did The Ancients Know?

The Sumerians

The Hammurabi Dynasty used a place value number system. This system was composed of both, base 10 and base 60 numbers in separate ways. This sexagesimal system, or base 60 system, goes back to the third millennium BC at least. Numbers up to 60 were built up based on repetitions of a wedge mark for 10, and a vertical stroke for a unit. This part of the system seams to be base 10. However the numbers were then arranged vertically. The first level we can think of as units. This line could be any number between 1 and 60. In the second level up, each of the numbers represented itself times 60. For example, a number of 5 on the second level represented 300 of the numbers on the first level. The numbers on the third level represented itself times 3600. An example of this is, a 5 on the third level would mean 18,000. Therefore, a number written as 5, 5, 5, would be 18,305.

The Sumerians, and Babylonians after them, became expert calculators within this system of numbers, and with it they devised one of the most useful of all scientific inventions, the table of numbers. The Babylonians could also solve linear and quadratic equations using these numbers. This was done readily by 1652-1531 BC. Over time, they had multiplication tables, tables for decimals, tables for squares and even tables for square roots.

The number 60 has so many prime factors we could assume it was used just for that reason. That assumption would be wrong. Where did this system develop? I believe it relates to the movement of the sky gods of the era. If it were an astronomically based system, it was also an energetically based system representing the 6 basic cycles of the gods, Sun, moon, Venus, Jupiter, Saturn and Mars. The divisions of the year were obviously measured by this system. For example, 72 degrees x 5 Venus cycles = 360; 30 degrees x 12 Jupiter cycles = 360 degrees. And this number 60 is also divisible by the 30 year Saturn cycle. Not so clear is the Venus/Moon Relationship (one Venus cycle is also divided by 20 moon cycles).

The ancients also discovered the movement of their gods were not precisely accurate. During their observations when they recorded these movements, everything did not always work out. This will be covered later, but it provides the essence for an even more sophisticated calendar.

They also observed the great sun's equinox day seemed to move through the star map of the zodiac. So, the last great cycle was born. The tracking of the equinox through its 21,600-year cycle could be tracked and recorded in the third level of the powerful base-60 number system. During the great summer sun time where the hot sun was king, the lion, king of the desert region, was developed as a symbol to mark this gate. We are just now beginning to realize the Sphinx, the great symbol of the lion gate. The equinox in the Leo part of the zodiac is probably in excess of 12,000 years old. Here I am again, ahead of my story.

The Egyptians divided the day into twenty-four hours we are told. Now let's look at that division. It's easy to see the day was divided into four six-hour units. Each of these was divided into 60 units (minutes) and again into 60 units (seconds). This is the system we still use today. It was apparently good enough to last at least five thousand years. Again we have the classic Sumerian base-60 numbering system, but it was modified only because it must fit the only thing more important than the heavens, our Mother Earth. The four six-hour periods, three of which can be absolutely known are, sunrise, high noon, and sunset. On the day of the equinox, this is the two six-hour periods and one twelve-hour period. But a probable need for balancing the two, six-hour daylight units, caused them to divide the night into two six-hour units also. The night sky could easily be divided by six, two-hour periods of the turning zodiac, but it was apparently not a short enough unit to be functional.

Another explanation may have been that in measuring the day they were interested in measuring more than time. If we go back to the most sacred of all units of measure, the Equinox Gate, and then look at the symbol we find the Eye-of-God symbol, the oval with a horizontal line dividing it equally. But if we chart the Eye-of-God symbol over time, it becomes a wave, a wave of light energy.

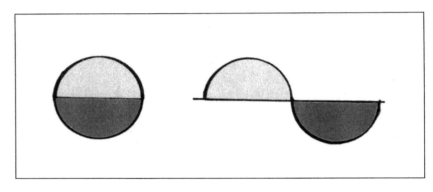

Graphic No. 9, Eye of God & Sign Wave

With the technology of the day it was possible to divide this wave into the equal parts we have described. When we add the hours, minutes and seconds we have a very minute scale. It must have been used for something when it was first developed. What, we can only imagine. This all seems like a lot of guessing, but many of our scientists are finding what appear to be very advanced technologies in some very ancient cultures. Some technologies we do not understand yet today. We will have a little more on this later.

The Sumerian Gods

Ur favored a local deity called Sin, a Moon god. Larsa and Sippar, both followed Shamash, a sun god. Several accepted Ishtar, later the planet Venus, but was, perhaps, a personification of fertility. Babylon was loyal to Marduk, a supreme creator God, Ahy heaven, Enlil Earth, Ea water. Most of the old Babylonian gods were cosmic.

The Gilgamesh Epic (ca. 2000 BC) has hints in it of a ritual of observing the sun, moon and planets over the tops of the distant peaks. *"There was on the mountain a gate through which the sun passed on its daily journey. Gilgamesh traveled eleven hours in utter darkness and 12 in what clearly represented twilight before coming out on the other side in a beautiful garden with jeweled shrubs."* (Note: The journey of 12 hours would be the length of night at the equinox when the sun would pass through the magical gate, during the Equinox 21,600 year march across the horizon). To explain the *"Gate symbol, Seal cylinders, "they often show the sun God stepping through a mountain pass between two gate-posts. Sometimes tarnishing the key to the gate."* (24) p 23. Others are lions on the gates, a common solar attribute, and solar rays issuing from god's arm.

There are no mountains in Babylon, so this may have been imported from the East or *"from the ranges that run northwest wards from there through present day Turkey."* (24) p 23. The omens related to the cosmos *"Enuma and Enlil."* (24) p 24. Many of these omens relate to the planet Venus.

The stars were also important sky beings. Some were used in noting important events. *"Helical rising, (first morning visibility) after a period during which the star rose only in daylight, was an important Egyptian calendar notation."* (24) P 14. The sun gets directly overhead on June 21 in Egypt. In the Northern Hemisphere the pole star would appear stable.

These pole stars would not swing the big ark. They would just appear to come and go, but a star that rose and fell near the zenith on the equinox would be quite consistent.

My guess is the very early Sumerian priest/scientist knew as we do these were not gods but simply "heavenly beings." I would guess they knew the "gods" were predictable and they could use this information to secure power and wealth from those that did not know the heavenly rules. Man, however, changes very little as we go through time, and many still use knowledge to secure power.

That is how I believe it was. A few knowledgeable priest knew what really was going on, but they used the information to make themselves appear as gods. In doing this, they eventually lost the knowledge and began to think of the sky beings and themselves as gods. We all know what is not shared is eventually lost. So the understanding of the energetic (wave like) actions of our entire solar system was learned, hoarded, used and then lost. We cannot afford to do this again. This time the knowledge must be shared with everyone. Let me now explain my reasoning for the above assumptions.

Rhythms of The Sky, The Mayan Calendar

I believe the great Mayan calendar is but a remnant of a much older and greater scientific work. As all great science, it was based both on observation and intuition. In his book, *The Mayan Factor,* Jose Arguelles helped make clear for me the relationship between the Earth, the Sun, the Moon, Venus and Jupiter. In doing this he reveals a culture, that for some, probably definitive reason, developed a series of observations of the sky beings and numbers to record them. To study the numbers and observations it is helpful if we become observers also. Much of Arguelles' book is beyond my understanding, but the chart on page 71 was of great help in understanding the original artifact.

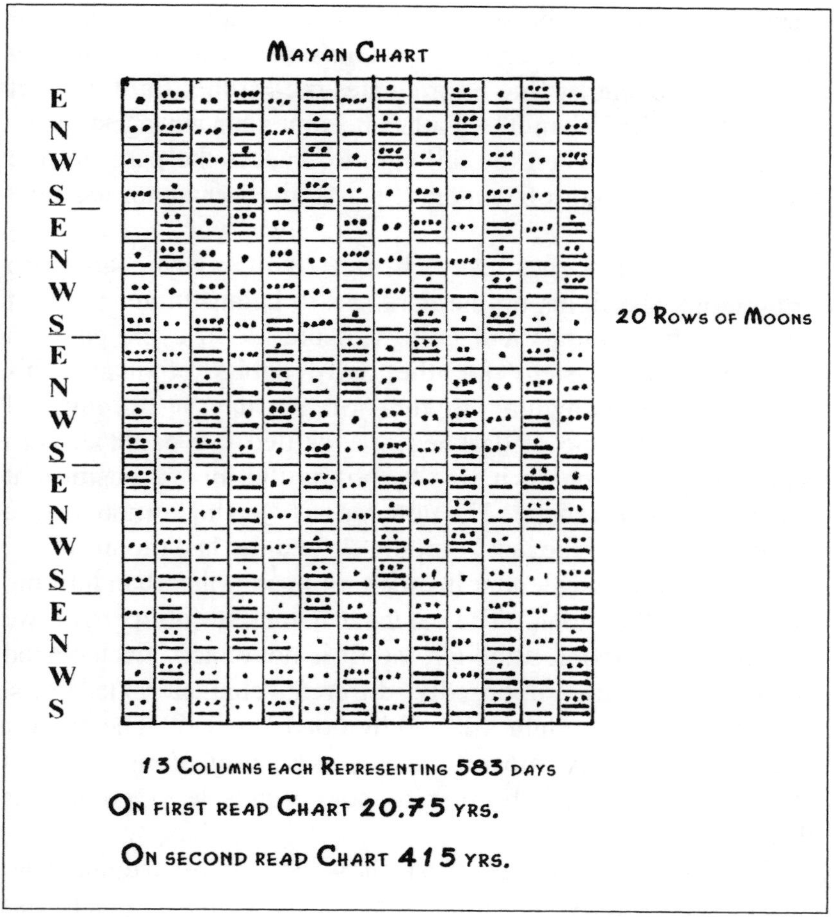

MAYAN CHART

E
N
W
S ___
E
N
W
S ___
E
N
W
S ___
E
N
W
S ___
E
N
W
S

20 ROWS OF MOONS

13 COLUMNS EACH REPRESENTING *583* DAYS

ON FIRST READ CHART *20.75* YRS.

ON SECOND READ CHART *415* YRS.

Graphic No. 10, Mayan Calendar Chart
Artist Sketch, (13) p - 71

Now, let's just become observers for a moment. The first big number is one, one sun, one day. The Father, Sun and our Mother Earth dance together in the circle of life we call a year. It goes around and around from birth to death to birth. In doing this, it passes through the sacred gates of the equinox twice

43

each year. All is in balance. The day and night are equal and this day can be measured exactly. This dance affects all life. In the spring the Father Sun impregnates the Mother Earth to start the cycle of life. Then The Father becomes his strongest at the summer solstice. Then the fall equinox marks the passage into the death-like sleep of winter. It starts all over again the next spring.

The second largest sky being (the moon) was also important. She lights up the darkness to balance the energy of the sun. The comings and goings of the moon cycle gave an excellent time system for the daily habits of man. This happened on a regular rhythm of 29 days (28 days of moonshine and one of darkness). A skilled eye could discern what day of the month it was by noting the moons position at sun set, or by it's shape. The new moon, $)$ the ¼ moon, D , the full moon, O the last ¼ moon, d and the last moon $($.

But the Mayan calendar is much more complex than looking at shapes of the moon. The calendar names twenty periods we assume to be moons, although the fit is not exact. Each period is different, with supposedly different characteristic traits. Why twenty, you might ask? Why not 12 or 13? The answer is found in the next most important sky being, Venus. It will take a more careful observer to note Venus as it progresses through its cycle.

We will start with the first show of a faint evening star, almost drowned by the setting sun. Then, Venus begins to rise in the evening sky getting brighter each day. Part of the way up it appears to stop rising and begins to fall back toward the sun getting ever brighter. The brilliance seems to peak just before it is again drowned by residual light of the sunset. In its final act it seems to plunge into the sun (the fires of hell).

That Venus is swallowed up by the fires of hell (the Sun) is well expressed in the ancient Sumerian poem, *Inanna's Journey to Hell* (N.K. Sanders, 1971, Penguin Books). That, however, is getting ahead of the story. Strictly from observation,

Venus is not visible for several days. Then, lo and behold, early risers see the morning star appear. Within a few days its brilliance is apparent. It rises further and further into the early morning sky until it reaches an apparent peak. Then as it starts its descent back to the sun it gets dimmer and dimmer. One day, it is no longer visible in the morning sunrise. It stays hidden behind the sun longer this time, but once again appears, as the evening star.

This process takes an average of 583.96 days or 19.77 moons. It may well be visibly related to twenty moons depending on when it is first seen. Now we have the second part of the Mayan calendar, but already we can see the moon is not a critical part of the count. It must have been important for weather and other observable reasons, but it was not a controlling agent in the calendar. First, it didn't measure a year very well, and now we see it didn't measure a Venus conjunction very well either.

If the moon isn't the key to the calendar than we must see if Venus can be. Here we find the answer. If we use 583 days (whole numbers are important) and multiply it times the number 13, also a key number in the Mayan calendar, we get 7,579 days. Now if we take Earth's year 365.25 days and divide it into our number of days we get exactly 20.75 years.

The Circle of Life, Earth's year, already has four identified points, two of which can be measured to the exact day (the equinox). When we put the two observations together, 13 Venus cycles will fall on one of the Earth's sacred four numbers. Now we have a flawless calendar of 83 years.

Some might still question this, reasoning it still too difficult to distinguish or recognize. We can look further. After Venus, the next most obvious sky being was Jupiter. We now ask the specific question. Where is Jupiter in the sky every 20.75 years? To our amazement, Jupiter also appears to be in the same place in the sky every 20.75 years.

So now we have it! Jupiter and Venus appear over the four main cardinal points of the sacred Earth circle every 20.75 years, marking off a perfect 83-year cycle to the exact day. This explains some of the key elements of the Mayan calendar. The twenty named moons or periods, the 13 cycles of Venus, and the four sacred directions, which are in reverse order, East, North, West and South (see chart).

There can be little doubt the original calendar used to create the Mayan calendar came from observing the rhythms of these four beings, Mother Earth, Father Sun, Venus and Jupiter. The sacred numbers of one, four, five, thirteen and twenty were all used. The question, implied by Arguelles and also first in my mind was, why did they do this? There appears to be much more here than is readily evident.

The Mayans had created a very sophisticated number system by this time. I doubt they needed a calendar to count the days. Perhaps, it was kept for strictly religious purposes, but I also doubt this. I believe it was related to energy levels much as Arguelles states. I think this energy could be observed in the weather and presumably in the people themselves.

To review how this model was developed, I want to restate the process that you can more easily picture the planet's cycles. I started these four planets from an imaginary straight line out from the sun. I called this line zero degrees, the fall equinox. I then progressed them in their orbits at their average daily movement, to a high detail, for 583 days. Every 583 days, I printed a line of locations in degrees. I then divided these degrees by 360 so the answer could be read in cycles and parts of years in the Earth column. In the Earth, Venus and Jupiter columns the partial years can therefore be interpreted to mean Heliocentric locations.

Compare Cycles for the Planets						
	Earth	Venus	Jupiter	Saturn		10/7/98	
0	0	0	0	0			
583	1.59615	2.59612	0.13454	0.05414			
1166	3.19230	5.19224	0.26908	0.10828		Move per Day	
1749	4.78846	7.78836	0.40361	0.16241			
2332	6.38461	10.38448	0.53815	0.21655		Earth	0.985617
2915	7.98076	12.98060	0.67269	0.27069		Venus	1.603093
3498	9.57691	15.57672	0.80723	0.32483		Jupiter	0.0830767
4081	11.17306	18.17284	0.94177	0.37897		Saturn	0.03343
4664	12.76922	20.76896	1.07630	0.43310			
5247	14.36537	23.36508	1.21084	0.48724			
5830	15.96152	25.96120	1.34538	0.54138			
6413	17.55767	28.55732	1.47992	0.59552		Note	
6996	19.15382	31.15344	1.61446	0.64966		Venus could be 1.60212	
7579	20.74998	33.74956	1.74900	0.70379		Small error in 1991	
8162	22.34613	36.34568	1.88353	0.75793		made it look better	
8745	23.94228	38.94180	2.01807	0.81207			
9328	25.53843	41.53792	2.15261	0.86621			
9911	27.13458	44.13404	2.28715	0.92035			
10494	28.73074	46.73016	2.42169	0.97448			
11077	30.32689	49.32628	2.55622	1.02862			
11660	31.92304	51.92240	2.69076	1.08276			
12243	33.51919	54.51852	2.82530	1.13690			
12826	35.11534	57.11464	2.95984	1.19104			
13409	36.71150	59.71076	3.09438	1.24517			
13992	38.30765	62.30688	3.22891	1.29931			
14575	39.90380	64.90300	3.36345	1.35345			
15158	41.49995	67.49912	3.49799	1.40759			
15741	43.09610	70.09524	3.63253	1.46173			
16324	44.69226	72.69136	3.76707	1.51586			
16907	46.28841	75.28748	3.90160	1.57000			
17490	47.88456	77.88360	4.03614	1.62414			
18073	49.48071	80.47972	4.17068	1.67828			
18656	51.07686	83.07584	4.30522	1.73242			
19239	52.67302	85.67196	4.43976	1.78655			
19822	54.26917	88.26808	4.57430	1.84069			
20405	55.86532	90.86420	4.70883	1.89483			
20988	57.46147	93.46032	4.84337	1.94897			
21571	59.05762	96.05644	4.97791	2.00311			
22154	60.65378	98.65256	5.11245	2.05725			
22737	62.24993	101.24868	5.24699	2.11138			
23320	63.84608	103.84480	5.38152	2.16552			
23903	65.44223	106.44092	5.51606	2.21966			
24486	67.03838	109.03704	5.65060	2.27380			
25069	68.63453	111.63316	5.78514	2.32794			
25652	70.23069	114.22928	5.91968	2.38207			
26235	71.82684	116.82540	6.05421	2.43621			
26818	73.42299	119.42152	6.18875	2.49035			
27401	75.01914	122.01764	6.32329	2.54449			
27984	76.61529	124.61376	6.45783	2.59863			
28567	78.21145	127.20988	6.59237	2.65276			
29150	79.80760	129.80600	6.72691	2.70690			
29733	81.40375	132.40212	6.86144	2.76104			
30316	82.99990	134.99824	6.99598	2.81518			
30899	84.59605	137.59436	7.13052	2.86932			

Graphic No. 11, Venus and Jupiter Chart

As stated the Earth's whole numbers can be read as years and parts of years. For example, 20.749553 can be read as twenty and three-fourths years. At the same time we can see heliocentric locations for all three bodies are as follows:

Earth .7496 (.749553)
Venus .7496 (.749552265)
Jupiter .7494 (.7494437278)

If all bodies are in the same place for a set cycle, a viewer on Earth will also see the same thing for each cycle. Therefore, a view of a brilliant Venus and Jupiter together in the evening sky, with a new moon on the spring equinox would only happen every 83 years. (Sometimes the moon may be off a few days. These would be sacred days). When the equinox is used as the trigger, the exact 83-year cycle would be correct to the day (four 7,579 days cycles or thirteen Venus 583 day conjunction cycles). This was also the sacred number of fifty-two (4x13=52) (As my editor noted, the number of cards in a deck). Of course, originally the deck of cards represented the 52 separate sets of circumstances that could occur. This was when the predictions were no longer understood to be created by the movement of the gods and were instead thought to be the will of the gods. The deck was then used to discern the will of the gods.

This calendar reads 7,579 days or 20.75 years. Four of these readings equal the first 83-year cycle. With the additions of the directional symbols, the base number of twenty multiplies the chart again (4x5). On this second reading, the chart shows 151,580 days, one and one quarter more than a perfect 415 years. It is my belief the scientific value of the chart is exactly 415 years within this culture.

For the ease of use, the Mayan number system was developed to read 400 at the second level, the product of 20 times 20. However, here we need to remember the difference between a purely mathematical number system of base twenty and an energy-related calendar based on the actual observable movements of the planets. In the second case, it can be assumed the planetary locations and cycles were actually the information being recorded.

This calendar, once understood, could be checked with common knowledge and an accurate equinox mark such as the one I discovered in Canada that is noted in my previous book, *Ancient Mines of Kitchi-Gummi*. A calendar, that is correct to the exact day for 83 years and repeatable, would install confidence in the science of any culture. With the addition of their directional marks, the nearly, perfect 415 year period can be read.

Because of its 30-year cycle, Saturn also tends to synchronize with the Jupiter cycle on the 60-year mark. This leaves the only other readily visible planet, Mars, out of synchronism. Maybe this is why the ancients called it the god of war. It should also be noted that the zodiac was the scientific map upon which these cycles were drawn and recorded.

Cycles upon Cycles, Jupiter/Saturn Conjunctions

I go clearly beyond the Mayan Calendar now and deeper into the history of ancient Sumerians in search of the 360 degree circle and the base 60 number system. To do this, I stick with the idea that observable characteristics of the great sky beings will lead to the answers. Since the Mayan calendar does not use the 360-part division of the sacred circle and yet uses Venus and Jupiter, it is only logical to look yet farther out to Saturn for the answer. We know Saturn's trip around the Sun takes about 30 years; therefore two cycles would give us the number 60, but how exactly was Saturn used?

Pieces of history, the fire cycle and the use of the Venus conjunctions lead us to develop the conjunction cycle between

Jupiter and Saturn. As might be expected, here we find the answer. The same system to develop a chart was used as in the previous example. The average movement of each body is multiplied by the average number of days in the conjunction cycle period. See the chart below.

Jupiter Saturn Conjunction Cycles						
No.Days	Jup. Move	Jup. Loc.	Sat. Move	Sat. Loc.	Ear. Move	Ear. Loc.
0	Degrees	0	Degrees	0	Degrees	0
7251	0.083077	1.67331	0.03343	0.67334	0.985617	19.85197
14502	0.083077	3.34662	0.03343	1.34667	0.985617	39.70394
21753	0.083077	5.01993	0.03343	2.02001	0.985617	59.55591
29004	0.083077	6.69324	0.03343	2.69334	0.985617	79.40788
36255	0.083077	8.36655	0.03343	3.36668	0.985617	99.25985
43506	0.083077	10.03986	0.03343	4.04002	0.985617	119.11181
50757	0.083077	11.71316	0.03343	4.71335	0.985617	138.96378
58008	0.083077	13.38647	0.03343	5.38669	0.985617	158.81575
65259	0.083077	15.05978	0.03343	6.06002	0.985617	178.66772
72510	0.083077	16.73309	0.03343	6.73336	0.985617	198.51969
79761	0.083077	18.40640	0.03343	7.40670	0.985617	218.37166
87012	0.083077	20.07971	0.03343	8.08003	0.985617	238.22363
94263	0.083077	21.75302	0.03343	8.75337	0.985617	258.07560
101514	0.083077	23.42633	0.03343	9.42670	0.985617	277.92757
108765	0.083077	25.09964	0.03343	10.10004	0.985617	297.77954
116016	0.083077	26.77295	0.03343	10.77337	0.985617	317.63151
123267	0.083077	28.44626	0.03343	11.44671	0.985617	337.48347
130518	0.083077	30.11957	0.03343	12.12005	0.985617	357.33544
137769	0.083077	31.79288	0.03343	12.79338	0.985617	377.18741
145020	0.083077	33.46618	0.03343	13.46672	0.985617	397.03938
152271	0.083077	35.13949	0.03343	14.14005	0.985617	416.89135
159522	0.083077	36.81280	0.03343	14.81339	0.985617	436.74332
166773	0.083077	38.48611	0.03343	15.48673	0.985617	456.59529
174024	0.083077	40.15942	0.03343	16.16006	0.985617	476.44726
181275	0.083077	41.83273	0.03343	16.83340	0.985617	496.29923
188526	0.083077	43.50604	0.03343	17.50673	0.985617	516.15120
195777	0.083077	45.17935	0.03343	18.18007	0.985617	536.00317
203028	0.083077	46.85266	0.03343	18.85341	0.985617	555.85513
210279	0.083077	48.52597	0.03343	19.52674	0.985617	575.70710
217530	0.083077	50.19928	0.03343	20.20008	0.985617	595.55907

Graphic No. 12, Jupiter/Saturn Conjunction Chart
(Note that the Earth Location Column also registers years.)

On the third line of this chart, we can see five of the Jupiter cycles (5x12=60), which nearly equal two of the Saturn cycles

(2x30=60). The Jupiter cycle is just long by .01993 parts of a rotation or 7.1748 degrees. The Saturn cycle is long. It is off .02001 parts of a revolution or 7.2036 degrees. If it were not for these small differences, the Jupiter/Saturn conjunctions would divide the circle of life exactly into six parts. The balance here of the six-part division led these ancient scientists to develop the following system of whole number parts. Using the whole numbers 12 and 3 for 36 and the whole numbers 5 and 2 for 10, we can create the 360-part division of the circle of life. Since Venus' sacred number is 5 also, the system is now complete. We call these divisions, degrees. It is interesting to note, the 360-degree circle is not just a sloppy measure of the 365.25-day year as some suggest. You may ask, how do you know that? Below, I will show you the answer is in the little parts we call errors.

As noted above, the small errors threw the system out of balance 7.2 degrees, for every three 7,251-day cycles. If we divide 360 degrees in the circle by the 7.2-degree error we discover it will take 50 cycles for the two great sky beings to be in balance again. To find the length of the cycle in years, just multiply 3 x 7,251 x 50 to get 1,087,650 days. Then, divide it by 365.25 to equal 2,977.82 years. In short, the fifty-year Jubilee of the early Hebrews may well have been fifty cycles. This may have originally measured the long cycle of approximately 3,000 years. Does Venus also show up at this conjunction? I can't really tell by my data, but my assumption is yes.

I don't make this statement facetiously. A few years ago I went over to a college for a Christmas star show. The astronomer presented what he believed may be an accurate interpretation of the Star of Bethlehem and the three wise men story. If my memory serves me right, all three planets Venus, Jupiter and Saturn appeared in the eastern sky just before dawn. This could well be what was called Jubilee, and it could have happened on or near the winter solstice. This would have been a great day in the eyes of those who worshipped the sky beings. My data is not accurate enough to check this out, but it is worth noting. The legend of The Three Wise Men from the East or The Three Sky Gods in the East to welcome the new Christ child would all start to make metaphoric sense if the translation is off just a little.

The fine points make interesting assumptions, however I suppose any good college observatory could clear it up for me. Regardless, it is evident enough from the figures I have how the circle of life was divided. It was the numbers five times twelve equal sixty for Jupiter and the numbers two times thirty equals sixty for Saturn. Together, these factor numbers make up the three hundred sixty degree divisions of the solar year. If the 360 degrees were just a poor guess at the number of days per year, the fifty-cycle Jubilee recorded in our Bible would have been meaningless.

There are three legs to the Jupiter/Saturn conjunction map, and two distinct equinox marks each year. Therefore, to arrive at a second definitive date, one conjunction leg must progress 180 degrees (see graph No. 2). This is actually twenty-five times the approximate sixty-year cycle or, approximately 1,500 years. As we draw these two triangles on the circle of life, the Earth year, we see the Star of David, so called because it was adopted as a symbol of the ancient Hebrew culture.

The early scientists must have known the length of the solar year as observed at the equinox sites. It is possible that later Hebrew tribesmen lost the delicate concepts of the nearly 3-thousand year cycle and just preserved 50-cycle Jubilee as a ritual. But, it would not have been possible to develop all elements of this early culture's mathematical and astronomical systems without knowledge of the fifty cycle moving error of 7.2 degrees.

It is now easy to see how the 60 base numbering system, was developed. Every sixty years the Jupiter/Saturn conjunction came back to approximately the same place in the sky (only 7.2 degrees off). By adding a second level to the number system, 3,600 numbers were achieved, and with a simple third level, a total of 216,000 numbers could be developed. We must remember this was a numerical system. It developed from, and loosely mimicked, the movement of Jupiter and Saturn within Earth's two equinox points, but it did not have an actual energy basis.

A second possibility exists. Originally, the Hebrew 360 day year was really measuring the sacred Jupiter/Saturn laps, not the Earth year at all. They would have had to constantly adjust to Earth's year if this was done, and I found no proof they did this. In fact, their calendar progressively got further and further off. This does not mean that at some time an earlier culture was not using both.

We have now shown how the 360-degree circle, the Star of David (the six pointed star) and the Sumerian sixty-based number system were developed. My proof, although somewhat lacking in fine astronomical detail, I believe, makes the point. We must remember these calculations were made using equinox marks and sun temples like Carnac. Considering this, we can forgive them for averaging the variable cycles of the errant Sky Gods. With the limited technology available it is phenomenal that they could develop this system so early in the Sumerian history. This does make a bit of a statement for the possibility of some holdover knowledge of a past-civilized culture. Although I by no means think it was essential. Some scholars, say whenever we see the base 60 number, it is like a Sumerian signature. This is helpful in studying these ancient cultures.

The Formation of Matter

We have been using these ancient two-dimensional forms to display the planet conjunction cycles. However, when the Ancients used the term Tree of Life, did they mean to convey more than simple weather cycles? Is the Star of David really the graphic presentation of two tetrahedra interpenetrated?

To think this way requires a leap of faith, but go with me for a minute. If we can learn to see the planetary cycles in this fashion, three dimensional, we can see the direct relationship of these vibrations to the formation of the building blocks of matter. Did the ancients recognize the Jupiter/Saturn cycle in the six petals of some flowers? Did they recognize Venus, the five pointed star, in the five fingers of our hands or the five points of some trees leaves?

Graphic No. 13, Stylized Star of David

For those of you who have been fortunate enough to read Lawrence Blair's book, *Rhythms of Vision* (copyright 1975), this is not totally new. Mr. Blair describes how the primary geometric solids are the building blocks of life. These are the tetrahedron, the cube, the octahedron, the icosahedron and the dodecahedron. (22) p 126 - 136.

The graphic presented above is part of seven circles. In addition to a tetrahedron, it includes a cube, the second basic building block of matter.

Tree of Life

We can see, if we modify the drawing and place one upon another, we have the Tree of Life symbol. This symbol has in it 19 circles. The 20th circle would enclose the whole but, holographically, steps it up one level. It should be noted here that this symbol is found on one of the most ancient temples of Egypt, The Temple of Wisdom.

When put into three dimensions, this becomes the icosahedron, the fourth sacred solid, and a solid of more complex life forms.

Graphic No. 14, Tree of Life Symbol

Just as a point of information on these last two solid forms, the fourth sacred solid, the icosahedron, is formed on the center of twelve spheres. It has twenty triangular faces and twelve points.

The last or fifth sacred solid is too complex to draw, but according to Blair, it is the last and most complex solid in human DNA. This dodecahedron has twelve faces and twenty points. As you can see, the base rhythms of the Jupiter/Saturn lap permeate all matter. That is why they are recognized as the Tree of Life. In the most complex forms of matter like man himself the Venus/Earth energy, this dodecahedron, is also incorporated into form. This little example should open the door and help explain how these large cycles are repeated in all the forms of matter in this solar system.

The Loss of Balance and Harmony

The Hebrew culture developed out of the same system that the Sumerians did with one exception. The nomadic Hebrew culture adopted their religion (one god) instead of science as the home of this information. Where-as, the Sumerians used the many gods in their science-based religion.

The conjunctions of Jupiter and Saturn as they move through the Zodiac became the basis for the 360-day calendar. Ignoring the small 7.2-degree error roughly every 60 years led to the loss of balance with the Earth Mother and the Sun. This was the end of what I call the Sun Worshipping Culture in the Middle East. More correctly, this is what I would call, the Sun/Planetary Harmony Culture.

Subsequently, the Hebrew, Judeo/Christian, social structure had lost its scientific base. The triangle conjunctions, as they clicked off the 60-year triangle precisely every 3 conjunctions and moved 7.2 degrees on the Earth Mother year, were no longer needed nor understood. This was apparently not relevant to the nomadic tribal sheep-based culture. Their nomadic life style did not permit maintaining a large observatory with its meticulous records. The twenty-five cycles between the equinox points was the magical number between the opposing points on the Star of David. The Star itself became the standard instead of what it represented.

The whole number 50 times the 7.2-degree movement was enough for the religious scholars. The abandonment of the equinox marks and the energetic harmony-based system removed the scientific base from the understanding. The sixty-year cycles, of 360-day years, was accurate enough for the needs of the Hebrew culture.

In the religious arena it became a duel between the one true God of the Hebrews and the misunderstood many gods of the Philistines and Egyptians. This disconnection from the Sun/Earth Mother rhythm was what was to become the point of loss of the (scientific) energy-based knowledge for western man. The energetic science based part was lost and only the religious part survived. Man saw himself and his physical world separate from God.

Much to my chagrin, this separation of God and science is still with us today. I personally do not believe there is a conflict between God and science. In my view, the Creator God uses his law (our science) to create. The only problem is we do not fully understand them.

Within the Moorish and Native American cultures, the harmony-based information survived this first crisis. Later, it was nearly destroyed in Carthage by the Romans and in South America by the Spanish. Lucky for us, in the Moorish libraries of Spain, some of the documents did survive. These documents gave rise to the European Renaissance when they were discovered in about 1400 AD. However, even though some of the secular knowledge was rescued, the separation of man from his God persisted. A few of the South American documents and artifacts also survived, an example of this is the Codex and the Mayan Calendar. As we are now, 500 years later, just beginning to learn what we have lost, maybe we can give respect to these great cultures for their wisdom. However, it appears we would prefer to focus on a culture's shortcomings than recognize their achievements.

The Mediterranean knowledge base went out when the Greeks conquered the Minoans and Egyptians. Although the many gods were kept, the scientific base was lost to the general society. Only the masters were able to recognize the values. Eventually, the Roman war machine destroyed even this. The real destruction with regards to our Earth Mother was the Roman power war machine we still worship so strongly today.

Now we have numbers without meaning. The number system (base ten) no longer records balance. It has become a technical numerical system, secular in nature. With it ended the knowledge of: shamanism, balance, harmony, vibration and a magnetic sense. All of these things we must now search to reclaim.

Stonehenge

You may wonder if these cycles were ever recorded or kept track of by the even more ancient peoples. Perhaps, you will recognize the drawing of the sixty-year Jupiter-Saturn-Lap triad cycle as the clock ticks off the two 30-year Saturn cycles around the year.

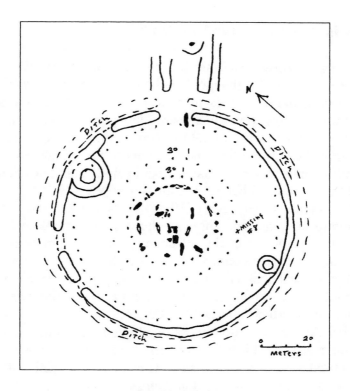

Graphic No. 15
Sixty Bluestone holes at Stonehenge (Authors Sketch
Of Official Ground plan of Stonehenge) (32) p - 82

As you can readily see here on this sketch of Stonehenge, the sixty years are clearly depicted as two thirty-year rings of bluestones, marked 1-30. This means that approximately 5,000 years ago, these cycles were common knowledge of the Monolithic Sun Cultures. I have already proposed this information had radiated out from the early Sumerian culture, but this is just supposition. It could just as well have been left over from a much earlier, civilized culture with an advanced knowledge of these cycles.

59

How is this Important Today?

We now come back to the Reality A effect. We have surmised this as the magnetic pull or bonding of Jupiter and Saturn with the sun. This increases the intensity of the solar radiation by somehow increasing air pressure and causing clearer skies and more radiation to pass through or to be lost. Was this the information the ancients were concerned with? Did these ancient people have a better understanding then we do of these cycles? I believe the answer is yes.

As stated earlier, every 19.85 years Jupiter and Saturn come into conjunction. Three of these conjunctions make the approximate 60-year cycle. Of course, these conjunctions take place in different sections of the Earth year. I believe the weather effects that I explained earlier were the reason this information was kept. This knowledge allowed the priests to predict future effects and maintain their power.

I believe we can do the same thing today, but for more holistic reasons. This next Jupiter/Saturn conjunction is now fast approaching as we have said. This leg of the cycle will be a serious problem again for the Northern Hemisphere. It will happen on an azimuth of 302 degrees or about July 22. This will be on November 3, 2020. Serious droughts will take place in the centers of large continents, like Russia, China, Siberia and the great plains of the USA. This will be along with scorching heat and wild fires.

This problem will be well under way by the actual conjunction. A sunspot cycle peek on September 22, 2010, along with an Earth/Venus/Jupiter harmonic, with Saturn in opposition, will make 2010 a year of very serious drought. This sunspot cycle will stay high through 2011 and 2012. The spring of 2012 will be very dry. Some relief can be expected mid-summer of that year. Some relief can also be expected at the bottom of the sunspot cycle in 2015-2017, but by the summer of 2019 the drought will be back on and the sunspot cycle will be rising.

The summer of 2020 and 2021 will again be a disaster for the Northern Hemisphere.

Is there any more evidence of this type of ancient knowledge? The answer is yes.

The I-Ching

This is the most ancient model to predict energy I am aware of. I think it proves the knowledge was there. The fine points are not really important in the description of this model. The Chinese I-Ching, in my view, also records Reality A locations. Here, we have what is referred to as the "Yang" locations. These are high influence situations. There is also the opposite, the "Yin" location; these energies are described as weaker or non-existent. A binary system is used to describe each of the visible sky objects. These appear as the 64 symbols in the ancient writings.

Graphic No. 16
A sample of I-Ching Symbolism (8)

The bottom line in the symbol represents the sun, the next up the moon, the third is Venus, the fourth is Jupiter, the fifth is Saturn and the sixth is Mars. Each is represented as a strong yang (solid line) or a weak yin (broken line) influence. In this way, the ancient people who introduced the I-Ching to the Chinese people had documented the Reality A energies (probably magnetic and/or other photon-based effects) of the entire visible solar system. They also provided a written summery as to how these various energies affected humanity.

As mentioned earlier, you can see in the graphic above that the I-Ching is a binary system. The implication of on/off also fits the concept of energy. Some may not believe this, but the information was confirmed later by spirit.

Discussion with Mr. "B"

R: "OK, I was wondering about this I-Ching thing, and it being almost like an Earth signature - like a solar signature, for our solar system." *B: "It is a solar signature: it is not almost like it."* R: (Chuckle) *B: "It is"* R: "Do other people know this?" *B: "Some, of course."* R: "Is there any one I can work with?" *B: "Mmm …. There probably is, but it would be time consuming because there would be language barriers and all kinds of obstacles, shall we say, and you really don't need it."*

R; "You said I was right in saying the I-Ching was an energetic model of the solar system. Was it developed by the Sumerians and taken to China?" *B: "Yes."* R: "By way of the Yellow Sea, and that (Yellow) river?" *B: "Yes"*

(Later) R: "This morning as I woke up I had a lot of" . . . *B: "Yes, you are a most willing student"* (with considerable expression*). R: (Laugh) "I thought that must be you. Umm, . . . this business about 60 the number . . ." *B: "Absolutely correct"* R: "Everything as I have it written down?" *B: "Your theory is correct, as we have instructed."* R: "I still have some unknown stuff." *B: "But you will be gaining insight to the unknown stuff, as you call it. Please give us time."* R: "OK." *B: "You are willing, but we do not wish to overwhelm you"*

R: "I have wondered about this for some time. When I put the cycle, for example the Earth cycle, the sun portion the dark and the light? The yang portion would be the sun portion and the yin portion would be the dark portion." *B: "Yes."* R: "And with the moon, I'm not sure. Would the full moon be yang or the dark of the moon?" **B: "No, the full moon.** " R: "The full moon would be the yang?" **B: "It would be the exact correlation"**

R: "Then it gets confusing. When I get down to . . . I am assuming that the six I have are right: the Sun, Moon, Venus, Jupiter, Saturn, and Mars." **B: "Correct."**

R: "The external planets then . . . It would be the yang at that time when they are at the zenith?" **B: "Yes."** R: "and the internal planet would be yang at the time the conjunction is at its strongest?" **B: "Yes."**

R: "So then we have a very yin time coming up." **B: "Indeed we do. And we are including this universal we in that."** (This was referring to the date 5/5/2000 when all the planets were behind the sun.)

R: "Is that a time when things are going to happen?" **B: "There will be things occurring, but not catastrophic or cataclysmic at this time . . . Yet"** (The implication is there would be no Earth changes yet.)

More on the I-Ching

In this way, I confirmed the I-Ching was a simplified model of the effects of planetary Reality A energy on Earth and its inhabitants. Did this mean the ancients knew more about what happened in the Reality A area? Probably yes, maybe no. We can't say for certain. We can be quite sure, however, that they were much better observers than we are. They also knew of the effects this had on the planet's weather and their crops. They made it a career to watch the skies and use an energetic solar system model to make predictions. To assume they didn't know how it was created or how it worked is absurd.

Now here, some will like to jump in and say that maybe space beings gave them the information. At first this occurred to me, too. Maybe intelligence from "out there" told them. But, here is the problem with that.

The I-Ching has only six bars. If it were from much greater intelligence, they surely would have been aware of the invisible planets as well as the visible ones. But, the I-Ching only has 6 bars, one for each of the visible significant heavenly bodies: Sun, Moon, Venus, Jupiter, Saturn, and Mars. The three inside ones are the Sun, Moon and Venus (below). The three outside ones are Jupiter, Saturn and Mars (above).

The structure of the I-Ching itself, the 64 binary symbols, testifies that it was created as a model of energetic waves as they were observed on Earth before the invention of the telescope. The system even had a way of recording changes for yin lines, presumably ascending and descending. The terms above and below were used to describe the two halves of a symbol and imply an understanding of the structure of the solar system.

The I-Ching model and the Zodiac map locations were used for several millennia. Some used it for the explanation of various human emotional states, and others to advise kings. This continuous use of these documents has a probable basis in fact. Literally thousands of ancient pictures and written documents have been discovered on both sides of the Atlantic concerning the signs of the Zodiac. We must conclude there was a very sophisticated culture that developed these two energetic models, understood them and used them as a base for the religious doctrines of cultures that still use them. Gregg Braden in his tape, *Awakening to Zero Point*, says a zodiac star chart over 30,000 years old was found in Egypt. This leads us even more strongly to the concept of a long past intelligent civilization.

Knowledge is sometimes lost and then, again, found. I believe this is what my work on Realities A and B represents. Although we no longer sit on mountaintops and watch the stars as a religious process, we still do it as a scientific process. Although our priests no longer record the weather when Jupiter is in Aquarius, the civil (weather) servants dutifully do. The scientists look at the results and make recommendations and predictions. "Take your umbrella today." "Lookout, there may be tornadoes, etc."

Now we observe the weather as if it had no cause, as if it were just a jumble of separate things that happen—too complicated to ever figure out. Maybe God is mad at us so he gives us some El Nino storms, or a drought every 20 or 60 years. At least our ancestors tried to figure out which gods were doing the dirty work. They may not have known how or why, but they knew their six gods influenced their lives and tried to appease them.

I am hopeful the small bits of truth I have been given will blossom in the minds of readers and stimulate synergy in fertile minds of others around the world.

Mr. "B" on Ancient Knowledge

R: "Is there a relationship between the 64 human genetic codes and the 64 I-Ching energy descriptions?" **B: *"There is a very distinct relationship. And I perceive you will find it very interesting . . . Umm . . . study that in great depth."*** R: "If I try to go to . . . The I-Ching would probably is the best place to start?" ***B: "Indeed."***

(Later) R: "I've come to the conclusion that the relationship between the I-Ching and human DNA is that human DNA has evolved 64 aspects, and these aspects are somehow resonant with the 64 different energy patterns of the I-Ching. Is this accurate?" ***B: "It is correct."*** R: "And then when a child is born those aspects (energies) that are present in the universe trigger like an imprint in that baby. Is that how it happens?" ***B: "Umm."*** R: "Or is it just with them all their life?" ***B: "It's pretty much - It's not actually either one of those things, but the latter is more close."***

R: "And then if we think of the genetic links being turned on by the emotion, then is there some energy turning on these certain . . . Is there a relationship then between the way the energy turns on in the I-Ching . . . I'm not . . . Don't worry about this?" ***B: "But yes, there is."***

My questions were garbled, but Mr. "B", reading my mind wanted me to know there was an energy in the universe turning on the energy pulses between the planets, "the I-Ching energy," just like the energy, "emotion" turns on the switches of our DNA as described on Greg's tape.

3/1/98: R: "A few months ago I went up into New Jersey and took part in a sweat ceremony. During the ceremony I felt I should leave, and while outside, I became aware of a possible connection between this Native American ceremony and a possible ceremony at New Grange in Ireland?" ***B: "Yes."*** R: "Are these related?" ***B: "Yes, they are."***

R: "Could you explain this?" ***B: "They are both ceremonies that cleanse. But it cleanses beyond the toxins of the physical being, and it can transport one forward or backwards in time. If you have read much about the Kiva, the Kiva is the window in Native American where one time walks and the same principle applies."***

R: "Did I ever live there in the New Grange Area?" ***B: "Yes."*** R: "What would have been my life there?" ***B: "You mean*** *what era?"* R: "Yes, just anything about it?" *B: "Well. It was during the time of the Moorish occupation and you were . . . What is the term? You were like a captain of the sentries, the warriors, the guards. You departed at a very early age of about twenty-three or four. But, you were well-respected and revered for your abilities and your intuitive abilities, particularly."*

(Later) R: "You once said I lived in Ireland during the time of the Moorish occupation. I never really questioned that, but we don't have records of the Moorish occupation in Ireland. I'm aware of when it might have been. Was it during the copper shipping days?" (2450 BC to 1200 BC) *B: "Yes, it was"*

R: "What were the connections of the New England stone chamber makers and the copper mines of Lake Superior?" *B: "Well, it was the same."* R: "Group of people?" *B: "Yes."* R: "I thought that, but I wanted to confirm it." *B: "Yes."* R: "OK."

R: "When I was looking at the Mayan calendar and working out these ratios and cycles, it came to me that one of the (charts) photos looked like there was a relationship between the twenty moons of the Mayan calendar, with the four directions repeated five times. There was a relationship between that and the Cree syllabary." *B: " That is true."*

R: "OK. Then, did they use these, umm . . . did the original first syllabary, then describe these energies?" *B: "Yes"* **(with emotion).** R: "I thought there must be some connection because of the direction stuff. And then was it just adapted to the language? But, the language still reflects some of those energies then?" *B: "Oh, absolutely."*

R: "That was one of the things I was thinking about a year or so ago. When I was working on these, and you said not to work on it yet, but maybe I should go back and look at these symbols." **B: "Yes, Now is more appropriate time, you have progressed so it won't be so difficult."** R: "OK. Can the words actually be charted like I did back then? Can you actually take a word . . ." **B: "Yes, you can"** . . . "and chart them in their parts?" **B: "Yes."**

This section refers to the idea that each sound in the original Cypriot Minoan syllabary, described in my first book, had a specific meaning. And, that this meaning made it into the sounds of the most ancient alphabets. Very ancient words could then be diagrammed to secure their meaning.

R: "One author says the Mayans came across the sea from Toulon. Were the natives (Implied South and Central America) that survived the last Earth changes influenced by the traders I was writing about around 2,500 BC? Or was it some other influence?" **B: "No, they were greatly influenced by the era of trade and the persons who were engaged in that activity."** R: "That's what the evidence seemed to point at, so I thought I would check it out." (I have put this in here to substantiate the connection between the Mayan and the Minoan and Sumerian cultures.)

But now back to our story. Before we leave the question of planets and the weather, in the next chapter I have developed a few basic proofs that show how we can benefit from a modern application of these principals.

4   Weather Proof Studies

We have developed numerous theories and assumptions. Some we have supported with anecdotal evidence, and others we have ask you to just believe. Now let's take one small step into a more hard science approach. This chapter concludes this section with a few studies that support the previous statements.

Venus Effects on Lightning Fire Starts

To start with, I want to show a simple graphic representation of the effects of Venus on fires. This regards the effect mid-summer Venus conjunctions have on lightning fires. The USFS Region Nine staff supplied the data used several years ago. The number of lightning fires was listed by year in graph form. The sample is substantial, representing all forests in a twenty state area for ten years. The results are impressive. See the chart below for the data.

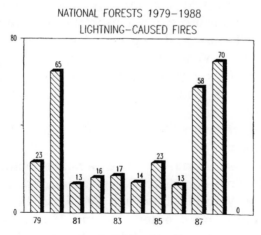

Graphic No. 17,
Lightning Caused Fire Occurrences, Region Nine, USFS

The results are: When the two Venus conjunction years, 1980 and 1988, are compared to the control years of 1979, 1981 - 1987, and 1990, there were 3.44 times as many lightning fires. This is a 344% increase over the average non-Venus conjunction years. When the year 1987 (a strongly influenced Jupiter year) is removed from the base, the Venus-years produce 454% more fires than the remaining eight base years.

This is damning evidence that a visit from Venus produces a lot more lightning fires. Some will ask, "What is the causal relationship?" All I can say now is it is just part of Reality B.

Venus Effects on Precipitation: a Local Study

The warming of the Earth has one more effect we can see described in the laws of physics. This second effect of Reality A can be somewhat verified by the small experiment I made and documented below.

As the Earth's atmospheric envelope warms, it will have a greater capacity to hold moisture. This would cause a net loss of evaporated moisture coming back down as rain. This reduced rain will cause a drying period in the time before the conjunction. After Venus passes Earth the heating effect must become less. This would cause the Earth's atmospheric envelope to cool, causing the extra moisture to fall as additional rain or snow. This is a simple law of physics. The question was, of course, how had this happen? So I did this small experiment.

A check was made of three weather stations on the Hiawatha National Forest for a five-year period, 1986 - 1990. There was a Venus conjunction on June 14, 1988. **The following results were noted: During May and June, the pre-conjunction months of 1988, only 33% of the average amount of rain fell, when compared with the average May and June rainfall of the four control years, 1986, 1987, 1989**

and 1990. This was quite spectacular, even though it was a small sample.

It was now time to check whether, after the conjunction, the extra stored moisture came down. **The post-conjunction months (July, August, September and October for 1988), registered 114% or 14% more rain than the four control years for the same period.** Due to the fact that the general warm period doesn't end until later in the early winter, heavier snow could be expected in November and December. However, the data were not collected at these stations.

This is a small test, but the hard data supports the assumptions that the Earth's air envelope is warmed by the internal passing of Venus that we know as a conjunction. I did this early work in the 1990s, but it helped motivate me to continue my work.

In 1999, I pulled together a more sophisticated study. It included the planets Jupiter and Venus. I will address one of these effects.

In Reality B, when Venus comes into conjunction with Earth, it warms up Earth's atmospheric envelope. This happens when it passes directly between Earth and the Sun. This warming also has a secondary effect on the moisture transpiration cycle within the Earth's atmosphere. An elementary law of physics that states explains this is, "The higher the temperature of air, the more moisture a given quantity will hold." I have prepared a small third study to prove this theory and I am presenting it here for your consideration.

Venus Warms Air During Conjunctions

I wish to restate my assumptions to make it quite clear what I am saying. When Venus passes between Earth and the sun, it causes the following things to happen:

- **The Earth's air envelope warms up.**
- **The air pressure becomes lower.**
- **The surface winds increase.**

These three things cause many secondary things to occur, but I will only discuss one here, *Earth's envelope warms up.* There are two effects from this warming: drought or reduced rain getting to the surface of the Earth as the conjunction approaches, and the air temperature warms. These are most evident in the month before the conjunction takes place.

Increased rainfall starts as the maximum heat level is reached, and the cooling phase takes place. This is very near the conjunction date itself. The increased rain follows for several months as the cooling weather removes the extra moisture from the atmosphere. In the north-central USA, this can also result in heavier than normal snowfalls.

This stored heat is not always easy to find. Sometimes it is not evident in the air temperature.

"What becomes of this heat energy used by evaporation? Energy cannot be created or destroyed, so it is hidden or stored in the invisible water vapor. When the water vapor condenses to liquid water or sublimates directly to ice, energy originally used in the evaporation reappears as heat and is released into the atmosphere. This energy is 'Latent heat' and is quite significant." Ruffner & Bair (26) p - 230.

Both of these effects are caused by the fact, as stated earlier, that the warming air envelope holds more moisture, and the cooling air envelope releases more moisture. I will exhibit this temperature increase in a small study I performed to show how it works. Remember, the key here was not to determine how much extra moisture was held, but to exhibit that warming does take place. Therefore, by law, more moisture is stored in the atmosphere. It also shows that this increased transpiration can cause drought, and the additional release can cause floods and extra snow.

The Study

Part One: A Noticeable Heat Increase Caused by Venus.

First, I selected four years when the Venus conjunctions were nearest the peak of summer, June 20. This is when the effects are less masked by other factors. These years are: 1964, 1972, 1980 and 1988.

To reduce the effects of Jupiter and Saturn, which can be very significant but more long term, I selected the control years for comparison as the year before and the year after the Venus conjunction year. For example, the control years of 1964 were 1963 and 1965.

Since proximity to the Great Lakes or oceans can also mask the effects, I selected three cities centrally located on a rather large landmass in the Northern Hemisphere. Since I am familiar with the fire history in Minnesota and Wisconsin, I started there. I did not use Michigan cities since the westerly winds crossing Lake Michigan dampened the effect. Maritime weather does not totally destroy the effects. It just makes them more confusing.

The selected cities were St. Cloud and International Falls, Minnesota and Eau Claire, Wisconsin. All three are located in the northern US, but west of the Great Lakes. A second reason these cities were selected was to develop the correlations between the effects of the conjunctions and extreme spring season fire behavior in this area.

This experiment could be replicated using many cities in central Canada's wheat regions or similar cities in Russia and

China. One key is that the vegetation must not be developed well enough to transpire much additional moisture. This would offset the increased temperature caused by the increased radiation. Part one of the experiment shows the temperature increase caused by Venus.

Since the objective was a simple proof, only two items were used: the daily high temperature at 1400 hours (2:00 PM) and the relative humidity at 1400 hours. This was recorded for all the days in May for the twelve years of data studied at each of the three cities.

It was my assumption that this would reflect the temperature increases. The relative humidity should remain about the same if some moisture is available. This would mean more moisture is being transpired to keep the humidity in balance. By selecting the northern cities, I could reduce this somewhat. This is the engine that creates the drought in the northern US— transpiration exceeds rainfall. As the ground and vegetation becomes dryer, as was the case in 1980, the number of days when the relative humidity was below 30% rose sharply.

The data were provided in degrees Celsius to one decimal point, and the relative humidity was to the nearest percent. The individual readings for each month were totaled and divided by thirty-one. So each year was represented by one figure, the average May temperature at 1400 hours. To maximize the number of samples, the Venus year was considered the base, and the control years each represented how much cooler it was than the base.

Table 1: Part A

City	Year	Venus Conj Deg. C.	Bef. Conj Deg. C	Aft. Conj Deg. C.	Diff. Deg. C.
International	1963		14.44		3.35
Falls, MN	1964	17.79			
	1965			15.15	1.78
International	1971		15.15		5.67
Falls, MN	1972	20.82			
	1973			15.97	4.85
International	1979		15.46		5.76
Falls, MN	1980	21.22			
	1981			16.4	4.82
International	1987		17.84		3.01
Falls, MN	1988	20.85			
	1989			117	3.85
Eau Clair	1963		17.67		4.04
WI	1964	21.71			
	1965			19.92	1.79
Eau Clair	1971		17.25		4.78
WI	1972	22.03			
	1973			15.76	6.27
Eau Clair	1979		16.22		5.38
WI	1980	21.6			
	1981			18.43	3.17
Eau Clair	1987		21.47		2.1
WI	1988	23.57			
	1989			18.8	4.77

Table 1: Part B

City	Year	Venus Conj Deg. C.	Bef. Conj Deg. C.	Aft. Conj Deg. C.	Diff Deg. C.
St. Cloud	1963		17.42		3.36
MN	1964	20.78			
	1965			17.33	3.45
St. Cloud	1971		15.42		3.89
MN	1972	19.31			
	1973			16.78	2.53
St. Cloud	1979		15.04		6.43
MN	1980	21.47			
	1981			18.15	3.32
St. Cloud	1987		20.77		2.58
MN	1988	23.35			
	1989			19.04	4.31

Data Source: *NOAA & NREL CD Rom;* **Solar Meteorological Surface Observation Network, 1961 - 1991, September 1993.**

Calculations: The high temperature at 1400 hr for the 31 days of May was averaged. The middle year is the Venus conjunction year and the controls are the year before and the year after. There is a 7.1-degree F. increase in temperature on the years Venus is in conjunction in June. The sample is very uniform. (Calculations = 95.2/24= 3.97 deg C. or 7.1 deg. F.)

Part One: Results

I had three cities, each with four Venus years. This gave me a total of 12 Venus conjunction samples. Since each year was compared to two years with no Venus effects, we had 24 actual samples. The table above indicates the differences in these samples. As you will note, the samples range from 1.8 degrees to a maximum of 6.4 degrees Celsius. They also group very well around the average of 4.0 degrees. Not a single control sample was warmer than its respective Venus month.

The difference in the average temperatures of May was 4.0 degrees Celsius or 7.1 degrees Fahrenheit. To put it another way, in these three cities, the average temperature at 1400 for every day in May would be _63 degrees F_. on all years that Venus was not a factor. Then, on the years of the Venus conjunctions around June 20th, the average temperature for each day in May at 2:00 pm would jump to _70.1 degrees F_. This is a substantial increase.

A second figure was recorded, the number of days in May when at 2:00 pm the relative humidity was 30% or less. As you would expect, this figure depends on the moisture available and the vegetation to evaporate it (transpiration). As they attempt to stay cool, the trees draw more moisture to balance their temperature with the increased heat. As the heat stress increases, more water is used to keep cool. This is the primary agent that creates drought during the warming process as Venus approaches. No real usable data were discovered. The availability and consumption of water would be necessary to show actual heat use.

Part Two: Hidden Latent Heat

When I tried to use the procedure in part one on cities further south, they reflected little to erratic temperature changes. This, at first, troubled me. Where could the heat have gone? Then I remembered *latent heat—the* invisible heat I described earlier. Since it was too time consuming to use individual hourly data to get stored humidity, I used an old weather almanac by Ruffner and Bair. This had monthly totals

77

for precipitation by year. I knew that in 1948 both Jupiter and Venus were in conjunction around June 20th. The data should exhibit the stored heat in reduced rain before the conjunction and increased rain after it.

Five cities were selected, primarily, because that is all I had in the appropriate zone. They had to be far enough South for transpiration to have started in May, and not so far south that the heat would cause extensive cumulus thunderhead clouds that early.

I then compared the monthly total rain from April and May (before the conjunction), and June and July (after the conjunction), with the monthly averages for these cities. The results were quite impressive.

Table 2

City	Year	April Rain	May Rain	June Rain	July Rain
\multicolumn{6}{c}{Venus Jupiter Conjunctions in June, 1948 - Rain Effects}
St. Louis	1948	1.32"	2.44"	5.12"	12.69"
Mo	Ave.	3.74"	4.12"	4.1"	3.29"
Omaha	1948	2.57"	0.56"	2.21"	5.91"
NB	Ave.	2.64"	3.79"	4.56"	3.67"
Oklahoma	1948	2.06"	4.19"	9.42"	3.54"
City, OK	Ave.	3.26"	5.01"	3.92"	2.76"
Rapid City	1948	1.62"	1.67"	4.86"	2.65
ND	Ave.	2.00"	3.14"	3.32'	2.29"
Kansas City	1948	0.80"	1.72"	5.45"	7.29"
MO	Ave.	3.40"	4.70"	4.82"	3.85"
All Cities	1948	7.65"	10.58"	27.06"	32.08"
	Ave.	15.07"	20.76"	20.72"	15.86"
	Diff.	-7.42	-10.18	6.34	16.22
	Below Av.	49%	49%		
	Above Ave.			30%	102%

Note: The Jupiter location on June 21, 1948 was 271 degrees, and the Venus conjunction was 270 degrees. (Ref. Weather of US Cities, Third Edition, Ruffner & Blair, 1987). (26) p 491-603

Part Two: Results

As the table indicates, the rain on the two months before the conjunction was *49% below* the average for those months. The rain on the month of the conjunctions was *30% above* average, and the rain on the month after the conjunctions was *102% above average.* This table strongly exhibits the above average evaporation, and storage of latent heat during April and May and the release of that heat as rain in June and July. It is my assertion that this heat came from the alignment of the planets over mid-summer and its effect of increased radiation, when it is the most potent in the Northern Hemisphere.

Well, this is it. I hope others will try to duplicate this in the cities with which they are familiar. The ramifications of developing and using the weather-influencing factors of Venus, Jupiter and Saturn are far-reaching. These cycles are absolute and can be modeled with precision. If I, with the aid of an ephemeras and a few tables, can explain a 7.1-degree difference in the average temperatures of May for three of the eight years in the Venus cycle, what could a professional weather modeler do on a good computer? That Venus cycle, by the way, repeats itself with only a very minor adjustment continuously. Instead of modeling the effects of these large weather makers, we could screen and model based on the defined set of parameters in the near future. This would tighten the system models substantially.

But, more important is the practical application of the resultant knowledge. Governments could plan and budget money for predictable periods of drought and serious fires conditions. Foresters could reduce, or delay, planting large numbers of trees in spring seasons that they know will have below average rainfall. Timber sales, or other work where erosion is a risk, could be planned when excessive rain is not expected. Accurate long range weather planning would be financially and environmentally beneficial.

Well, I'm anxious to hear from you. I can be reached at, Jewell Histories, 79 Ski Run Trail, Fairfield, PA. 17320, (717) 642 – 8342

Planets Affect The Weather: a Proof

When I approached a few weather scientists on this subject, I received the polite but simple response. What is the process? If you can't explain the process no one will believe your theory. Furthermore, extraordinary claims will take extraordinary proof. With this simple dismissal they went back to the safe position the weather is to complicated to figure out.

This somewhat disheartened me, but not enough to make me quit. It did make me realize, just like the academia connected to my first book, *Ancient Mines of Kitchi-Gummi*, that the academia connected to this book was going to be more of a problem than help. I guess it is much as one professor told me. *"You never get much new thought out of academia: they are too busy protecting their current ideas."*

With this in mind, I created a simple proof for those who say the planets do not affect the weather. I'm sure there may be some flaws in the logic, but I think the point is well made.

The following is a Proof to establish the process by which the planets affect the weather on Earth.

Point One: Only a fool would not know the sun affects the weather. If it were not for our sun, we would be a frozen lump of rock and ice sailing through the endless space. This is where the proof starts.

Point Two: We also know the process by which the sun heats the Earth. It is in the amount and nature of various rays that strike the Earth and its various surfaces, the atmosphere, the oceans and the land surfaces. You can prove this to yourself by just stepping into the shadow of your house on a hot day. Therefore, the actual process is not the question.

Point Three: Since we have established that the sun does affect the weather on Earth, and that the process is in the heating caused by its rays striking the Earth's surfaces, what is the real question?

I believe question number one is, are these rays constant? If they are, they may not be responsible for changes in the weather. However, if they were not constant, this inconsistency by definition would have to affect Earth's weather.

Although a few may still argue the suns radiation is a constant, I think most scientists now agree that it does vary. This brings us to the following statement without need for proof or corroboration.

Point Four: Variation in the intensity or make-up of the sun's radiation can, and does, affect the weather on Earth. It is my contention that this point does not need to be proven.

Point Five: The real question then becomes: What causes the variations in intensity or make-up of the sun's rays, and is the sun's effect on the Earth caused by or reflected in the systematic movement of the planets?

If these weather effects are either, caused by or reflected in the systematic movement of the planets, then the planet locations should be built into the weather models to improve their accuracy. The essence then, of any proof, is to establish this relationship or prove no relationship exists.

Point Six: Scientists have for centuries stated that there was a relationship between the sunspot cycle and the Earth's weather variations. Some may still question this but, by the obvious definition in the following statement, it must be true.

If we observe a black spot on the surface of the sun, by definition either the intensity or the nature of the radiation from that spot must be different. If it were not, we could not perceive any difference between it and the surrounding solar surface, therefore, seeing it makes it so.

From here we can extrapolate the following: The variation in numbers of sunspots, in some way, change the amount of or nature of the solar radiation striking the Earth.

This statement is also proven by the limitation that large or intense sunspot cycles have on our use of some radio waves in Earth's atmosphere.

Point Seven: Therefore, the ability to prove a causal or cyclic relationship between the movement and location of the planets and the number of sunspots, would mean their cycles could be used to predict with some accuracy the sunspot cycles. By definition then they could be used to predict variations in the amount or nature of the solar radiation striking Earth.

Point Eight: Now we move beyond simple points of logic to pure scientific investigation to see if this has already been proven. I will reference three great well-written papers on the subject. The first is by Rhodes W. Fairbridge and John E. Sanders. The title is *The Sun's Orbit, AD 750 - 2050: Basis for*

New Perspectives on Planetary Dynamics and Earth-Moon Linkage."

This is a long and complex article. However, several key points are made with which we are concerned. They determine that the cycle by which the sun orbits the center of the solar system mass (the Barycenter) is 59.577 years long (a triad), and that after three such cycles a period of 177.93 years have elapsed, the sun returns to approximately the same place with regard to the Barycenter.

They go on to establish that this is related to three of what they call the Jupiter Saturn Lap (JPL) cycles (19.859 years or, *"the pulse of the solar system"*). They determine this to be statistically correlated with about 30% for one factor and 50% for a second factor of the variation in the Sunspot cycle. It will help us here to understand the sunspot cycle is a complex variable cycle that averages about 11.1 years in length but varies from 7 to 17 years.

> *"In a comprehensive statistical analysis between sunspot numbers and various solar orbital parameters based on the computerized ephemeras, Pimm and Bjorn (1969) calculated that the statistical variance ranged from 10% to 50%. They found that the correlation coefficient between sunspot number and the factor we have emphasized, distance from the center of the sun to the Barycenter of the solar system, was .5547, which accounted for 31% of the variance. They found the greatest correlation (coefficient of - 0.7057) between sunspot numbers and the radius of curvature of the sun's path: this accounted for 50% of the variance of the sunspot numbers."* (29, p - 462)

Another way to say it is this. They have determined a significant percentage of the factors going into the complex sunspot cycle wave. And these factors directly correlate with the movement of the sun around the barycenter of the solar system. They have also determined that the locations of Jupiter and Saturn synchronies this movement of the sun.

They also developed a correlation with the moon's cycle. The moon cycle and the Earth cycle are inter-related and very complex, so I will not go into them here.

We will leave their fine study here and move to the work of Therdor Landscheidt of Schroeter Institute for Research in Cycles of Solar Activity, F.R. Germany.

Landscheidt: His paper is entitled, *Long - Range Forecasts of Solar Cycles and Climate Changes.* In the abstract he states:

> *"The secular cycle of solar activity, which seems to be connected with climatic change, volcanism, and the ozone column, is correlated with a wave pattern formed by secular variations in impulses of the torque driving the suns oscillatory motion about the center of mass of the solar system. Information about the epoch, phase, and amplitude of the secular maxima and minima of sunspot activity and concomitant solar-terrestrial effects can be read from this secular wave."* (30, p - 421)

Although the focus of the work is a little different, Landscheidt is still talking about the sun's movement around the solar system Barycenter. He, however, is focusing on what he calls the torque or variable forces being applied to the sun. This torque, of course, is what causes the movement and cycles described by Fairbridge and Sanders.

A second quote we need to put forth here is the last sentence of the abstract. *"The fact that climate is the integral of weather should lead to an improved understanding of variations in climate that are subject to solar forcing."* *(30, p - 421)* One additional other quote that I believe will be helpful is this:

> *"A strong 100-day cycle is formed by the change in angular acceleration of the vector of the tidal forces of the planets Venus, Earth, and Jupiter that shows a very strong relationship to energetic x-ray bursts." (Landscheidt, 1984) "The mean length of this cycle of 3.367 mo. and the harmonic of the torque cycle of 2.4 mo....." (30) p - 432*

Landscheidt quotes many papers. In one by Neubauer, a process is explained whereby the polar vortex is displaced, and the jet stream is similarly displaced. This was a result of warming of the stratosphere caused by magnetic storms that are, of course, a result of sunspot activity.

It is obvious to Landscheidt that it does no good to know there is a relationship to the sunspot cycles, unless and until you can predict with some accuracy these complex and variable cycles.

Many cycles are examined. One stands out. It is an 83 year cycle and its multiple of two (166 years). This is the frequency component with the greatest amount of energy of all the harmonics. Wolf had already found this cycle at the end of the nineteenth century. This harmonic was evident and could be projected in a period of 7,600 years from 5259 BC to 2347 AD. We need a quote here to avoid misinterpretation on this proof.

> *"The wave has a mean length of 166 yr. but each extremum, whether positive or negative, is related to a maximum in the secular sunspot cycle. ... And varies within 47-118 yr." (30)*

A third paper, I later pulled off the Internet, was written by Jean-Pierre Desmoulins. It was entitled, *Sunspot cycles, are they caused by Venus, Earth and Jupiter Syzygies.* (First, Syzygies are when two planets are at conjunction or opposition.) To quote Mr. Desmoulins abstract:

"Tidal waves on the sun culminate during syzygies of the tidal planets. Heliocentric syzygies and oppositions of Jupiter, Earth and Venus occur in bursts, and plotting these bursts shows a regular signal, with a 22 years period, in phase with the sunspot cycles for three centuries." Desmoulins (30) p - 1

Further along in his work, Mr. Desmoulins shows in graph form a near perfect fit of his information. It appeared that this electrical engineer, living in Grenoble, France, had solved the problem of the source of the sunspot cycles while working on it as a hobby. I had enough experience working on it to believe he might be right, so I tried to duplicate his work.

It was really quite simple. I just prepared two charts, one of the Venus/Jupiter syzygies and one of the Earth/Jupiter syzygies. To get a long-term fit I needed to go out two more decimals than Desmoulins. The Venus/Jupiter period became 118.42 years and the Earth/Jupiter period became 199.535 years. Then I simply correlated the Julian dates of each list. The dates that were exact or very close would yield the greatest effect.

In the period between June 22, 1948 and February 8, 1997 five peaks existed with an average of 152.46 sunspots per peak. These peaks fit the sunspot curves perfectly for the five cycles. It appeared Mr. Desmoulins work was accurate. It was also evident that the bottom of the sunspot cycles was controlled by the more minor affects. The affects of Mercury and Saturn would have to be figured in order to get the whole cycle.

But working only with the peaks one more piece of information was evident. The distance between the two syzygies peaks was exactly 3,790 or 3,789 days. Using 3,789.5 days and doubling it, I came up with 7,579 days or 20.75 years, the exact length of one pass through the Mayan Calendar. It was evident that the Mayan Calendar had been designed to predict the weather, based on the movements of Venus, Earth and Jupiter. I am sure they were not aware the tidal effects on the sun caused it, but they did know these "gods" affected the weather.

At this point, let's go back to Landscheidt. I think it is fair to speculate. Did he know the Mayan Calendar is 83 years in length? Did he also know that it is based on the harmonics of Earth and Venus conjunctions, in sync with Jupiter and the Earth's four seasonal points, the equinox and the solstice events? I believe, if he had, he would have been able to state that the correlation between planets and sunspots is unmistakable.

In essence, like the Jupiter Saturn Lap (JSL) Cycle, the Venus/Earth conjunctions form a predictable cycle. There is, of course, one difference; it is much shorter. It moves about the sun like the JSL cycle but on a different speed. Every eight years it completes five conjunctions. These conjunctions take the form of a five-pointed star instead of the triangle of the JSL cycle. What the 83-year cycle is could be described as the *Venus/Earth/Jupiter* Harmonic.

Point Nine: I think, by now, it is safe to say these good scientists and many before them have already established that there is a direct relationship between the cycles and locations of the planets and the variations in the sunspot levels. These have been pointed out carefully, and in detail, in all three of these articles. The first two quotes come from a conference on climate published in 1987, which was plenty of time to have incorporated this into our scientific models. The problem seems to be that these great weather minds don't have a good enough grasp of the astronomy involved. Only Desmoulins, an amateur astronomer with enough general scientific and computer skills, had been able to solve the problem. The others appear to have all the necessary information, but are doing nothing about it. However, it may not be a problem of these scientists at all. Maybe they were just not believed. They may just have been unable to move the *lethargic academia.*

I believe I have demonstrated that a relationship exists between planet movements and locations with the sunspot activity levels. The waveform we are looking for is long and very complex. The 178.73-year JSL cycle moves at one pace around the sun. A second wave, which we will call the *Venus/Earth/Jupiter* Harmonic cycle, moves around the sun in 166 years.

Although I am not a mathematician, my gut tells me that if these two cycles were to lap, they would create the long cycle we call an Age (166x11 = 1826yr) (1826x12 =21912yr.).

It seem painfully obvious to me that the movements of the planets cause these sunspots. The problem is, we are attempting to see the relationships without building the models. It's a little like trying to keep your eyes on one big ball and nine little ones as they swirl around in a washing machine. We need to put a solid solar astronomer with a good computerized ephemeras in a weather station and start recording weather in the cycles, first the short ones and then the longer ones.

Point Ten (the last point): If I leave the scientific proofs behind and go back to the cycles kept by the ancients, maybe we can wrap this up. The JSL cycle is really the ancient Star of David Cycle. Each triad of 59.577 appears to move 7.2 degrees on the Earth's year as it repeats itself. In this way, the ancient Sumerian and Hebrew clocks counted off the years. It took 16.666 cycles to move to the next triad location.

Concerning the range shown in sunspot cycles, "*Kanda (1933) pointed out that systematic changes through time caused its period to vary between 10.38 yr and 11.28 yr.*" (9) *p - 462.*

If we take the mid-point of this range we get 10.83. By multiplying 10.83 x 166 we get 1,797.78 or 1800 years (The length of an age on the ancient calendar). If we added twelve of these Ages, we have 21,600 years, the cold/warm cycle of Michael B. McElroy, (Graphic 18, Chapter 5), as published in his article "Changes in Climates of the Past: Lessons for the future." (4)

In the ancient Toltic Legend we can again see the numbers. The 83-year cycle times 22 = 1,826, again the length of an Age. *"13 heavens and 9 hells"* = 22. This is a direct quote from the legend. (18)

From the ancient Middle East, 59.78 actual years or 60-year Hebrew cycles form the Star of David.

From the Fareast, 60 x 9 = 540, the number of statues on the old temple approach in Anchor Watt (540 x 20 = 10,800). There are 10,800 verses in the Rig-Verde of India (10,800 times 2 = 21,600 years) or 540 x 40 = 21,600 years in the warm/cold weather cycle from the ocean sediments of McElroy. This covers an 800,000-thousand year record.

So, there it is. The ancients had it and used it in their calendars. Presumably, it told them the weather or something of value. The Mayan Calendar reflected it. Evidence of the knowledge goes back for 5,000 years. Some of the weather researchers have it, and they seem to be challenging their associates to use it. An Earth physicist found it in an 800,000-year physical record on the sediments of the ocean bottom. What more do people want? The planetary cycles affect the weather here on Earth, pure and simple.

5   Earth Weather Change

I would like to address a second aspect of the Earth weather. This is the phenomenon called "Earth Changes" or "Pole Shifts," now being predicted by some. In reality, we mean here, catastrophic Earth weather changes.

These forecasters call themselves "Students of the Ascended Masters." They have for us a new map of the sphere we call Earth. They say they receive this information from channels. What are we to do with this new prophecy in our own time? How should we react? What does it all mean?

As the millennium turned over, there were great expectations coming from many different corners of the world. We dust off the books of the old prophets, we listen closer to the old native shaman stories, but as the number changed to 2000 nothing really noteworthy happened, at least on January 1, 2000. Should we now go back to complacency and business as usual? I don't think so. Now the summer of 2000 has passed, and it was the worst fire season in fifty years in the western USA. These major changes and cycles may seem to move slowly to us, but that doesn't mean they are unimportant.

What do the past predictions reveal?

We have always had our visionaries and our seers. Recently, I watched a TV show on Leonardo Da Vinci, a well-known artist and seer. There also are the Revelations of John in our family Bibles, the Nostradamus predictions, Hopi Indian legends, and Edgar Cayce, the sleeping prophet. All tell us cataclysmic changes are coming. Even the survivors of the last great Earth changes all seemed to get warnings, if we can believe our Bible and other old legends.

90

Is it prudent to ignore this type of information simply because we do not understand it, and cannot set a date nor say it will happen at 2:00 tomorrow afternoon? As a conservative and a scientist, I tend to look back, as the visionaries look forward. Is there anything, that as a man, I have observed that would lend credence to any of these seemingly wild claims?

Earth's Cycles: The Ice Caps

The physical world, Earth, the "Blue Orb," the third rock from the sun—is there any proof that might lead one to think it would shift on the axis it spins? How could this happen? What might the result be?

We all know the poles of our spinning world, like most other spinning worlds, don't get direct rays from the sun. The angle is very low, and for that reason very little warmth is available to be absorbed. What there is must be distributed over a large area. Therefore, an ice cap develops on our polar regions.

If the poles were to change, ice would form on some other part of the sphere. Has this happened? Well, yes it has. About every 125,000 years a great ice sheet has formed. These ice sheets expand and contract on a much shorter cycle. We will look at the last of these cycles. One sheet moved over North America and Europe. In my home state of Minnesota, we studied the last four of these glacial ice sheets because they left their mark on the soil and landscape.

I was always of the belief that the world got colder, and polar ice crept down in all directions from the North Pole. Well, it seems that really isn't true. There was no icecap creeping down across Eastern Asia or the Northern Coast of Alaska. In fact, these areas were for the most part ice free and apparently much warmer than they are today.

Now, our little lesson in solar physics tells us something is wrong here. If there was still very little sun, and Earth was getting colder, why was there no ice in these two areas? Even today, these arctic seas all freeze over each winter, though the weather is supposed to be much warmer. It is all but impossible to go via ship across the northern coast of Asia. Yet, no great glacier was there in the frigid Ice Age. In fact, we are told the mammoths were eating temperate vegetation as far north as the New Siberian Islands 20,300 years ago. How can this be?

We are told we had great glaciers to the 45th parallel, over Europe and North America, but the 75th parallel was ice free in Northern Siberia, and temperate plants were growing. It seems a more logical answer must be found. Could it be that the spin axis, or as we think of it, the North Pole, may actually have been 25 or 30 degrees toward the North America. This would explain the movement of the massive ice sheets. Now, it also seems this didn't just happen once, but something very similar happened at least four times, if the Ice-age history of Minnesota is at all correct.

Now, we have something to work with, a repetitive cycle causing the four great glaciers that crossed Minnesota to track in almost the same way. To do this, the North Pole would have to move to one location, then back to another location, then back again, etc. If this happened, is it far-fetched to say someday it will again move back to somewhere in Hudson Bay? In nature, we learn to recognize cycles even though we may not know the cause. The Neolithic farmers knew summer would return even if they did not know why. We should be at least as smart.

Will this happen quickly or slowly? We all know the glacial build-up, and ice may move slowly in the eyes of man. However, the actual spin change and cold weather may come at a much faster rate. There are two pieces of information that I am aware of even without any research.

But first two comments by Mr. "B" on this subject:

R: "It appears that the procession of the equinox is one of the keys to the glacial movement cycle?" **B: *"Indeed it is. "***

R: "There looks on the curves, as if there is a second, longer cycle imposed on this. One man suggests this would be CO_2 variability. I'm wondering, is that correct also?" **B: *"Yes, but you will discover an even greater impact of that."***

Woolly Mammoth proof: There have been many great woolly mammoths found in northern Asia that were apparently quick-frozen. The most recent was raised in March of 2000. We all could watch as the great beast was being chipped out of the ice. At one time a small plant, still green, was shown in the ice found below the body of the mammoth. Much was made of the size of the beast and how it was such a great accomplishment to lift it and fly it to its new home in a Russian ice cave. But, nothing was said of the conditions under which this freezing could have happened. How could a several thousand pound woolly mammoth be quick frozen with a plant still green under it, and last undisturbed for 20,300 years (a solid carbon date) without thawing or rotting?

In some of these finds, the meat is still supposed to be edible as dog food these thousands of years later. On *Northern Exposure*, a TV situation comedy, set in Alaska, mammoth was put on the menu at the local eatery. This is no doubt, hyperbole. However, the repeated finds do indicate there is much we do not understand in this scientific phenomenon.

Another interesting story is the discovery of a small frozen mammoth that the finders named Dima. It was found in June of 1977 in northeastern Siberia. This baby mammoth was frozen in a mudslide. The problem was, that mudslides were not part of the northern Siberian climate where it would be cold enough to freeze. Where it was found in southern Siberia, it was unlikely the little body could freeze without some decomposition.

The third and similar problem was the Brezovka Mammoth. It was discovered 70 miles north of the Arctic Circle.

> *"Examination of the Brezovka mammoth revealed that it was a small male. Un-chewed grass and buttercups were in its mouth and undigested vegetation in its stomach indicated death in mid to late summer. The original report states that the animal died "during the second half of July or the beginning of August." Its position in the permafrost had been one of setting on its haunches, with its pelvis bone, right foreleg and several ribs broken. The contents of its stomach consisted chiefly of field grasses; nine kinds were found, but no evergreens were present. ... The Brezovka bull evidently died of suffocation."* (5) p-19,20.

This presents the typical problem of the frozen mammoths. What could freeze and perfectly preserve a mammoth still sitting up in late July or mid-August in Siberia? I suggest the answer is: "nothing that we are aware of, but, obviously something that can happen here on Earth." Some of these examples are thought to have frozen as much as 44,000 years ago. Of course, the most recent date is much less than that.

I will go into one other problem mammoth. It was called the Mamontova Mammoth. This was an incomplete carcass found in Siberia in 1948. A man named Farrand described the weather:

> *"In general, the floral assemblage is richer ... somewhat warmer and probably also moister than the present flora of the tundra in which frozen mammoths are found."*

> *"Since the associated flora is that of a warmer lati-*
> *tude, an apparent paradox remains - That the climate*
> *in northern Siberia was warmer than at present at*
> *some period in late glacial time when climates else-*
> *where on Earth were cooler than present."* (5) p - 25.

These questions continually haunt those trying to explain the Frozen Mammoth Phenomena. Farrand had the courage to pose the question and write it down, more than our current researchers have done.

During the great ice age, 15,000 to 50,000 years ago, we know North Asia was a huge grassland with large herds of mammoth. If, during this ice age the North Pole was somewhere in the North Atlantic region, and then, if it suddenly shifted to its current location, this might explain why some of these giant mammoths suddenly found themselves in the deep freeze. It may also explain why the people could find enough bones to pick up and build houses with them. Why was there grass and not trees as there is today?

We have another great change, the weather patterns in Africa's northern Sahara. It used to be rainy but now it is a desert. Is this desertification or great changes in the weather patterns?

Recording a Warm Cold Cycle

Michael B. McElroy is an eminent mathematician, a Ph.D. in Applied Mathematics from Queens University in Belfast in 1962. He has received numerous awards and had published over 170 papers by the year 1991. One of his articles is *"Changes in Climate of the Past: Lessons for the Future,"* published in a summary of papers from a symposium called *Planet Earth, Problems and Prospects. (4)*

In this paper, McElroy does an excellent job of synchronizing one cycle that we know with the Ice ages. By using an eight hundred thousand year period and the cycle of daily insulation at 60 North longitudes for summer solstice. The calculated change in the heat levels of the sun reaching the Earth's surface is then compared to two different types of oxygen isotopes. These oxygen isotopes are taken from seashell sediments at different levels and are used, as a measure of how much of the Earth's water is stored in glacial ice.

The net result, when simplified, is this: The 21,600 year cycle, presumed to be the equinox procession, creates a very regular cycle of about 10,800 years between its peak warm period and peak cold period. This can be seen in the chart following. Although this cycle is quite uniform and is a significant factor in the Ice Age expansion and contraction cycle, it does not operate or explain the time frames alone. A second, more significant cycle of about 90-100 thousand years is necessary to fully explain the glacial cycle. But before we go on, let's look at this procession of the equinox cycle in more detail.

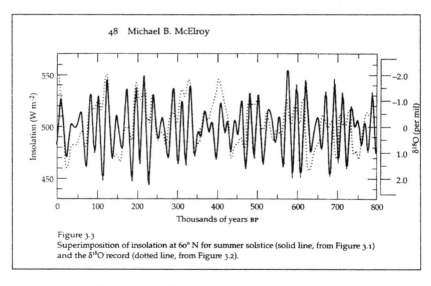

Figure 3.3
Superimposition of insolation at 60° N for summer solstice (solid line, from Figure 3.1) and the δ^{18}O record (dotted line, from Figure 3.2).

Graphic No. 18, Warm Cold Chart (4) p - 48

The Procession of the Equinox

Current observations by our astronomers, based on the very short part of the cycle that modern science has observed, indicate a rate of approximately 25,920 years for this cycle. This represents a somewhat troubling problem. Why the difference?

According to McElroy, over the last 800,000 years a clearly traceable warm/cold cycle exists. He said it was approximately 21,000 years. When I use his chart, I can count 37 cycles in the 800,000 years sample. This calculates to 21,622 years. If I drop the 22 years, I get a cycle of 21,600 years. We must realize here that this is simply an actual historical record being generated by state of the art science.

This coincides very well with our earlier work on the sun's movement around its barycenter. As we have pointed out in Chapter Three, these cycles were also known and used by the ancients. There seems to be strong evidence that the Mayan, the Ancient Hebrew and the Hindu cultures all had a system to measure the historic temperature fluctuations caused by the procession of the equinox. These were represented by counting the Jupiter/Saturn Laps. They used different terms, but it is apparent they were measuring an *Age*. Some considered it a cosmic year. Remember, the term *year* is often used interchangeably with cycle or circle. As the equinox progresses, the basic map these ages were recorded on was the *Zodiac*.

If we take McElroy's cycle length, 21,600 years for a cosmic or galactic year, and divided it by the twelve signs of the zodiac, we get 1,800 years for a cosmic or galactic month. This represents the hard data condition for 800,000 years of Earth's history. Now, why would I say ancient cultures knew and studied these cycles?

As I have already explained in the previous sections, the Sumerian culture had fully developed the base-sixty number system. This system alone could have been, and probably was, developed from observations of conjunctions of the planets Jupiter and Saturn, as they were mapped against the Earth year circle and the zodiac.

As a point of review: I want to repeat how we have seen this number 21,600 in the past. This information is critical to understanding this book. The number 216 or 21,600 is the key *harmonic* of our solar system. I believe the Mayan culture is an outgrowth of the Olmecs and Toltic Cultures. In his book, *Lord of the Dawn,* Tonie Schear translates an ancient Toltic legend. In this legend they talk of an *age* as eleven heavens and nine hells. Each of these is a cycle of their calendar. Schear translates this as 52 years (I believe this should be 52 cycles). As I have already pointed out on the Mayan calendar, 52 cycles really means 83 Earth years. The breakdown of heavens and hells definitely could relate to weather. Regardless, when we multiply 83 years by the number 22 (13+9), we get 1,826 years. This length of time that Shear translates to be an age comes within twenty-six years of our hard data galactic month of 1,800 years. When we multiply 1,826 by the 12 signs of the zodiac, we get 21,912 years for a galactic year.

We have already spoken of the Hebrew people inheriting the Sumerian number system. We know the Hebrew calendar is based upon the triad of the conjunctions of Jupiter and Saturn, a period of just under 60 years. If we take (60 x 60 x 6) we get 21,600 years per galactic year. If we divide that by the 12 symbols of the zodiac, we get 1,800 years per galactic month.

We can also see this number related in a fearful way in our Christian Bible, the famous 666 in the book of Revelations. This can be taken in the context of the pure numbers of the base-sixty system. In this system the first number represents 6, the second number represents (6 x 60 = 360) and the last number (6 x 3600 = 21,600). In this system all the numbers are added. This gives us 21,966. But we know the Hebrew year is short 5.25 days or only .98563 years. This means that the length of the celestial or galactic year would be 21,650 only 28 years from our hard data estimate of 21,622. The galactic month would be 1,830 years under this system.

I think it is safe to assume the dire predictions in the book of Revelations of the Christian Bible are associated with the celestial year. The symbolic 666 originated from the knowledge of the early weather cycle connected to the procession of the equinox.

One more culture reflects these numbers. It is in the ancient Hindu culture. Their text, the *Rig Veda*, reflects a half cycle of 10,800 years. They speak of the motion, as back and forth, so a half cycle is appropriate. This number is reflected in the number of stanza in the *Rig Veda*. The quarter cycle 5,400 years is reflected in the 540 statue arrangement at ancient Ankara also (25) p - 162,163. Of course, this reflects the actual full cycle of 21,600 again.

This is not irrefutable proof this was not the reason for these numbers, but it certainly leads one to wonder. It could well be these cultures were recording the cold and warm cycles of the celestial ages and were depicted them in there culture.

It seems altogether possible that an ancient source culture had and was using such information many thousands of years ago. If the periodic cycle of the procession of the equinox did change during the last pole shift, and is now 25,920 years, as our astronomers believe, it would now be impossible to generate these ancient numbers; yet they exist.

The recent studies of the Sphinx in Egypt as made and reported by Mr. John Anthony West, and if viewed with an open mind, could be helpful in putting dates and context to these weather changes. In these work Mr. West (30) indicates the Sphinx and the Temple of the Sphinx have both sustained substantial water erosion. The last time that it rained enough in Egypt to do that was about 9,000 BC.

Discussions with Mr. "B " on this subject

R: "I'm confused about this number 216. According to the works of Michael McElroy, there is a cold/warm cycle in our Northern Hemisphere that is about 21,600 years long. Its (basis is) an 800,000 year (period) with 37 cycles. I get a 21,621-year cycle. Is this correct?" *B: "Yes."* R: "Is this the progression of the equinox?" *B: "It is, but remember as this cycle begins to make its transition, your timing is not going to be 100% exact. Just as if you turn on a hot water faucet you don't get immediate hot water. Do you understand what we are speaking?"* R: "Do you mean the last Earth change has changed the cycle?" *B: "Yes."*

R: "So the 25,920 year cycle, I think this is what they consider is the procession of the equinox now. Is that accurate?" *B: "It's very close, but that is not exactly numerically correct. And I'm not at all certain that they have the ability to calculate it exactly."* R: "So the 800,000 year history is probably as accurate as we can get it then?" *B: "Yes."*

R: "I've found several cultures that seem to have numbers that comply to that." *B: "Yes."* R: "The Mayan culture has thirteen heavens and nine hells, and this is twenty two (the *Lord of the Dawn* legend). If you take 22 times the 83 years of their calendar, I get 1,826 years per galactic month. If I take that times twelve, I get 21,912, which is very close." *B: "Correct."* R: "And then, if I look at the Christian Bible, we find the number 666, in Sumerian (base 60 numbers), this would be 21,966 years. But, that's a short year, or, if I correct it, I get a 21,650 galactic year." *B: "That's correct."* R: "And when I look at the Star of David and do the calculations, there I get 3 times 600 years (1,800 years, a galactic month)." *B: "That too is correct"* R: "And that times 12 comes out to the 21,600 galactic year."

R: "So, there is one place in the book of   where they use 25,920 years for a cosmic year and they use 2160 for a cosmic month, but that wouldn't be accurate then." *B: "No, not ... That whole book is wrought with inaccuracies."* R: "I have other questions on that book. That's the most important thing I needed to figure out."

R: "Now I've read the Book, *Hamlets Mill.* Is this a good book?" *B: "Umm, ... It is good. It has some human errors."* R: "They have a basic number, it's 10,800, the number of stanza in the *Rig Veda*, and it's like a half cycle." *B: "That's correct."* R: "And they did talk about the Hindu tradition about "alternative motion." So, they were thinking of it as going forward and backwards. It makes sense ... It would be a half cycle." *B: " That's correct, because ... Yes."* R: "OK."

Now, let's make some assumptions

First, the Cycle: Anything as dramatic as a pole shift cycle must already be known. If the glaciers are influenced by the 21,600-year progression of the equinox cycle like many have suggested (or at least it may be part of the answer), this would give the ancients one good reason to track the progression of the equinox. It may also explain why the zodiac is so very ancient.

How do these curves fit the glacial periods and the great mammoth extinction covered so well in John White and Peter Ward's books? The great Ice-Age die-off, if I understand Ward correctly, started with a strong weather pressure on the Ice-Age populations about 11,000 years ago, with a more or less effective hunting population of humanity killing the final animals. This took place when they migrated to North America about 10,000 years ago. So far, it all fits.

101

These theories were all developed before I asked Mr. "B." When I did, I was in for quite a shock.

R: "One of the perceptions I've had, that back in the series of glacial periods 10,000 years, 20,000 years, 30,000 years, etc., that came over Minnesota, that these were caused by an approximate 15 degree shift in the North Pole?" **B: "Absolutely."** R: "And this may be what is going to happen?"

B: "Indeed. When the polar axis shifts, it disturbs all things on this planet but primarily the weather patterns. Now this is being exemplified in a very small way by what is commonly called, and laughingly referred to us, the El Nino. You can see very graphically how a slight shift in weather patterns can wreak havoc and devastation, or you can imagine if that is magnified by 360, what devastation can occur. And that is what occurs when the pole of your planet shifts."

R: "It's obvious this is a cyclic thing in the last 50,000-60,000 years." **B: "Oh, indeed, and it should not surprise anyone, yet it always does."** R: "Does it shift back and stay shifted for a long time?" **B: "Oh, indeed."** R: "What causes it to go back?" **B: "The same thing that caused it to shift. It is a magnetic fluctuation that is part of the galactic magnetic fields."** R: "So it goes beyond the solar system." **B: "Oh, indeed, way beyond."**

R: "You said one time there would be extreme winds during the pole change period." **B: "Oh yes . . . umm."** R: "But we probably won't be aware of them?" **B: "You will not be aware of them."**

6   What Could Cause Such Change

The Method of Change

First, the spin of Planet Earth has been going on since the beginning of the solar system. Like all the other true planets, it is probably a result of eddies and condensing of matter in the spinning disc of our solar system. I'm just guessing, but maybe as matter condensed, the Earth may have spun faster—just like a figure skater pulling in her arms and legs.

I believe this spin has never changed substantially since life began on the planet, or it would be extremely evident. If it had ever stopped, the sunny side would cook and the shady side would freeze. If it had stopped or reversed, what mechanism could re-start it? Look at Venus. It is probably a moon of the sun, more than it is a planet. It may have been captured, or possibly some contact stopped its spin. At least, it doesn't spin now, even though it rotates around the sun.

If we assume the Earth's spin is constant and gyroscopic, then we must accept the movement of, at least, some part of the outer crust. That is, if the poles actually move.

One thing that shows the Earth doesn't move at the 17-mile deep platelet level is that the Pacific Plate moves over a great vent in the Earth's crust below it. This movement is thought to have formed one of the Hawaiian Islands at a time. During an active period, an island is formed. Then the plate moves in an inactive period. Another island is formed in the next active period. Apparently this movement is very slow, millions of years, and at a detectable constant speed, which causes these islands. Therefore, the part of the Earth with this vent must also be ridged or semi-ridged and, generally, move with the crust as one unit.

This leaves only the movement at the deeper layer (a few hundred miles down) as the logical answer, if the poles actually move, as we have evidence they may. None of this should come as any surprise to a scientific mind willing to take a speculative look at the evidence. One of John White's theories seems to have the greatest probability for how the actual pole shift may take place:

> "*The solution, Thomas says, comes from the work of the Swedish physicist Hannes Alfven, who discovered the effects of a combination of magnetic, electrical and physical forces ... Thomas identified the magnetohydrodynamic energy (MHD) of the Earth when affected by galactic-scale null zones of zero magnetic energy, as the means whereby the magma layer changes it's properties in the direction of greater liquidity and freer flow. These null zones exist between concentric spheres of magnetic energy that fill the galaxy. Their effect on the Earth's magnetohydrodynamic energy in turn makes the magma layer a lubricant for the solid crust, allowing it to slip around as it is pulled...*" (5) p - 149

Here we have a scientist who has actually described the galactic waves referred to by my guide, Mr. "B". He also mentions the null zone that I questioned Mr. "B" about later. The magnetohydrodynamic energy was explained in this way. In a simple experiment, he was able to show mercury was very fluid in a normal state at room temperature. However, if an electric current surrounded it, it became more rigid. It was about this experiment that I later spoke to Mr. "B". For more information, refer to John White's book, *Pole Shift.* (5)

Why have I included this diverse, and to most people, far-out pole shift in these same writings that I started about the planets? It is simply because the space soup that we were starting to prove in Part One of the book has turned up in the research for Part Two of the book about pole shifting. One interesting thing about the MHD theory is that it gives us something to put into the space soup to cause the effects we are seeing.

Theory

As in Part One, I am going to introduce a few new descriptions here. We have all heard of deep crust pizza and thin crust pizza; here we need to do the same thing. First, when we think of the Platelet Earth Crust (PEC), we are talking of an area that most people are now aware of. The platelet tectonics, although relatively new, can be described as those parts of the Earth crust between the rings of fire. They are presumably about seventeen miles thick.

A second term that I would like to propose here is the Deep Earth Crust (DEC). This crust is made up of the PEC and a semi-ridged part right below it. It goes down to a layer of lighter rock about two hundred miles deep. It is slippage at this deeper level that we are discussing here.

We are going to go one step further and suggest that if a pole shift took place, it was at the DEC level instead of the PEC level. The reasoning here is simple and straightforward. The movement of the whole Earth's crust at the plate level would have to be reflected in the location of the string of islands that we call the Hawaiian Islands. It seems that the relationship between the vent hole in the deeper layer below the Pacific plate, and the plate itself, is predictable and ancient. Therefore, during the ice ages, either the Earth's crust didn't move, or it moved at the deeper level.

We are presuming that it could have, in fact, moved at the deeper level and still be consistent with the weather history that we are aware of. Let us state clearly what we are saying. The outer one fortieth, or about the first 200 miles deep of the Earth's crust, may have slipped about 2,000 miles. This would move it from a point where the North Pole would have been, somewhere around Hudson Bay, to where it is now in the Arctic Ocean. To be stated another way, the Hudson Bay moved 2,000 miles away from the pole along the 85 West longitudinal line; Siberia moved north 2,000 miles along the 95 East longitudinal line. These locations are strictly guesses and could easily vary in either direction.

As stated earlier, it is my belief that the spin is basically constant. The outer crust (200 miles deep) may be able to slide without disturbing the spin too much and without major breakage of the PEC along the Ring of Fire. Any major breakage would have probably wiped out most of the life on the planet. That didn't happen.

This minor shift would have created havoc with the world's ocean currents and air currents. These would have been able to force massive changes in the Ice-Age mammal populations, desertification of the Sahara in Africa, etc. In fact, sixty genera of species did go extinct during the last Earth polar shift (Ice Age).

I am not going to try to prove or disprove the case for the Earth changes, as they are being predicted. We are simply going to relate how the physical properties of the Earth and the Solar System and, possibly, galactic realities may make these changes possible or probable.

If more information is desired, there are several books available on speculative pole shift processes. The book by John White, *Pole Shift,* was important for this section. In it White covers most of the significant theories in a very thorough fashion.

We have stated a few of the reasons why many think only a pole shift can explain some of the world's weather history. The most difficult effects to explain are the glacial movement in the past 30,000 or so years and the quick freezing of mammoths.

Is this Possible?

Now, is this possible? What could make it happen in a sort of cyclic fashion? The key information that we have just learned from John White's book is important. This simple little electrified mercury experiment, along with the knowledge of the extremely liquid layer of Earth 200 miles deep, as Mr. White says, provides a key to understanding one element of the possible process. But, what of an actual trigger? What could be the trigger? Well, our space soup, of course. If the existence of Reality A or Reality B can be shown to be simply the difference in magnetic field charge we on Earth are passing through, why then can't we push it further? It could also explain why the magnetic poles seem to shift back and forth ever so many thousand years. In this process of shifting back and forth from positive to negative, wouldn't it cross a null point as described by Hanes Alvin? At these null points, why wouldn't the inner rigidity of the DEC relax, and let the magnetic Earth center come back in line with its surroundings in space. This would act much as a solenoid does in electrical switches?

My early work of the planet effects on the weather seems to support elements of Chan Thomas' theory for the pole shift. This theory says nothing about time; only the professionals have the instruments necessary to read that. It appears many common people are becoming caught up, in this Earth-change drama. But, if the Earth's magnetic field is getting less pronounced, as Mr. White suggested in 1980, maybe it is time someone checks these theories. Responsible science must deal with threats to the species. Why else do we try to understand the world we live in? Anything less and we may see disasters that would make hurricanes look like child's play.

I believe I now have established at least theoretically that Reality A exists. The ancients even observed it and called it the

"Yang" energy. They created a model called the *I-Ching* where the energy existed or it didn't; and if it didn't, it was ascending or descending, coming close or going away. This was covered earlier. Some may not grasp this totally, but for those of you who don't, we are going to end here and accept this as a possible truth.

If the open space between Jupiter and the sun is filled with space soup, and if that space soup is charged and can alter the light energy passing through it, what is the process that is taking place? That process is our next area of discussion and exploration.

Magnetic Theory

Using the clues in *The Pole Shift,* I believe we need to use the magnetic model of the activity. If light energy actually travels within a magnetic media, or is "influenced" by a magnetic media, it is the logical culprit. We can theorize this then as Reality A. Is space soup in a magnetic state that can alter the light passing through it? It is not a great leap then, since light travels through most of the space in the universe. Most of the space in the universe is made up of a magnetic field. Using this as an assumption, it then holds that as our solar system expands out through the magnetic field of our universe. The iron core of Earth will generate its own magnetic field.

This is simple physics. An iron bar, moved through an electronic field, will create its own electromagnetic field. The Earth has a magnetic field. If the speed at which the iron bar is moved through the field is constant and the greater solar system's magnetic field is constant, the magnetic field of the Earth would remain constant, and the poles would never shift magnetically.

However, the Earth's magnetic field is not constant. It is variable, and every so often, the poles do switch altogether.

This clearly leads one to assume that the space soup electromagnetic field is not constant, but variable. If it is variable, and it does reverse polarity on a regular basis, we could describe it as one of nature's sine curves.

The sine curve is, more accurately, the record of passing through the variable field. This curve meets all the requirements of our assumptions to this time. It is variable. It is both positive and negative, and it remains in balance as all things in nature that are stable must.

Now, let's go back to our factual observations. We know the polarity has reversed every X number of years in Earth's history. Our theories tell us that this history may have been observed as a sine wave curve with the magnetic field of Earth recording this sine wave of magnetic history in the formation of cooled magna on the ocean floor. We must remember here that we are only reading the magnetic tape of Earth's history.

If I apply our theoretical process to this history, I must assume that the space soup we are passing through lies like alternate layers of magnetic particles, first arranged in one way from positive to negative for a while, and then switched to negative to positive for awhile.

As you can readily see, as Earth passes through these various bands of charged space soup, it will also have to pass through a period or spaces where there are no charged particles, as can be readily seen in the photo below (Iron filing photo). When iron filings are sprinkled on a common refrigerator magnet, they arrange themselves in bands with spaces between them. No particles are allowed between them. The space is totally free of space soup, or at least, any space soup that can carry a magnetic charge.

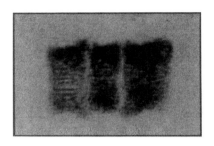

Graphic No. 19, Iron Filings over Refrigerator Magnet

In Graphic No. 20, two much stronger magnets are forced together, North Pole to North Pole and taped into place. A large amount of iron filings were sprinkled on the magnets. The filings were forced out of the space between the powerful magnets. This is essentially what will happen between the galactic bands of charged photons.

Graphic No. 20, Space Between Two Strong Poles

Therefore, the existence of space soup that is magnetically charged and in large bands, could explain the magnetic pole reversals that are recorded in the rocks of Earth.

It also gives us a new thing to worry about. What happens when the Earth passes through the uncharged space soup, or if you will, the area of no space soup at all? We can assume, unless the laws of physics no longer apply, that the Earth will no longer have a magnetic field. A few questions arise: Would electronic things work? I really don't know. We can be sure that compasses won't work. But, will other electrical things work? Now, we must take a very large leap of faith to propose such a theory. We have only a few examples, when we as mankind have observed, that electrical appliances and things don't work. Yes, I'm talking about the eyewitness reports of UFO sightings. Witnesses often say the electrical equipment of the car did not function.

If we assume here that the UFO object somehow disrupted the magnetic field or absorbed the magnetic field in the immediate area, we have the following idea: A car battery that we assume is totally self-contained, and a car radio that is self-contained, do not work. So we have something going on in the electronic equipment that requires a magnetic field for it to work. I really can't take this any further, because I just don't know and can't conceive of the physics. But the potential is that all electrical equipment may not work. If we take this to one more level, our mental reality is based on electromagnetic brain waves. We know we are theoretically dead if all brain wave activity stops. Well, at least, we say we are dead. The progressing theory here assumes we are electronic beings. Maybe, removing us from any electromagnetic field can simply shut us off.

Recently, I heard the U.S. military might even have a weapon that removes or disrupts the Earth's magnetic fields and renders all electronic equipment useless. There may even be a weapon to stun people. It's anybody's guess what the military is doing.

A case for pole shift

We have all read of the last great Ice Age, when so much water was tied up in ice that the oceans were 130 meters shallower. This is called The Last Glacial Maximum, and it took place about 21,000 years ago. William L. Donn in a book called *The Earth: Our Physical Environment* produced a map showing the Earth rebound from this massive ice sheet. As some of you might know, the ice was several miles thick in some places. The sheer weight of the ice pushed the Earth crust deeper towards the core of the Earth. As the ice melted, the weight was released, and the Earth's crust responded by moving back out to where it belonged.

This seems all rather simplistic, and one might ask, "What does it tell us?" Well, if we look at the map of the uplift in Graphic No. 21, I believe the answer to this question is obvious. Why does this massive ice sheet have an epicenter somewhere in the area of the Hudson Bay, approximately 30 degrees south of the North Pole?

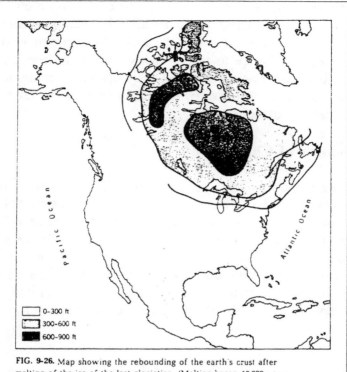

FIG. 9-26. Map showing the rebounding of the earth's crust after melting of the ice of the last glaciation. (Melting began 18,000 years ago and was completed 6000 years ago.) The region of maximum uplift over Hudson Bay indicates the region of maximum ice depression of the crust and hence the region of thickest ice. (Generalized after W. Farrand and R. Gajda. *Geographical Bulletin.*)

Graphic No. 21, Up-lift map (28) p - 314

This location cannot be related to the fact that this is on a landmass instead of ocean. We have an even bigger landmass in Asia, and there is no evidence that a large ice sheet covered it. We also have a large glacial ice shelf in Antarctica over the ocean known as the Ross Ice Shelf. Why, then, is the location of this ice sheet so far south of the North Pole that we have today?

I think we might revert to what we could call the obvious that the pole has moved. If the actual pole location were in the area of the Hudson Bay, then the lack of direct sun would be the reason for the ice to form. This would be in keeping with what we know of how our world works. To further support the concept of a pole shift, we would need to be able to say exactly when such a shift took place.

Calendar of Cataclysms

Recent technologies are correcting previous errors in our thoughts every day. I have just discovered an article that may go a long way toward establishing a realistic timetable for the period from 9,000 - 15,000 years before present. In the article, carbon dating of undersea sediments in the southern Caribbean Sea was compared to current base line tree ring data for about the first one half of the period. In this way, the carbon dating accuracy was pushed several thousand years deeper into the past.

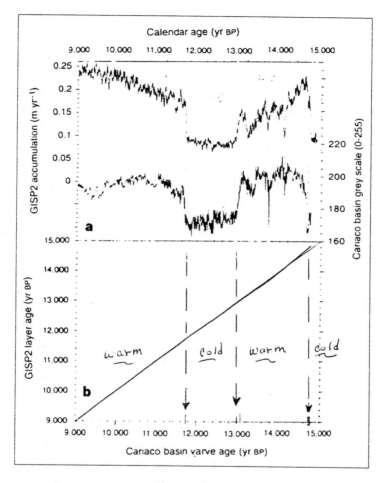

Graphic No. 22,
Warm / Cold, End Of Glacial Period (11) p - 66

The article, "*De Glacial Changes in Ocean Circulation from an Extended Radio Carbon Calibration,*" was prepared by a distinguished number of scientists. In this study, the radiocarbon data was from Varved Sediment in the Cariaco Basin in the Southern Caribbean Sea.

115

Large-scale abrupt climatic transitional events are recorded in these sediments. These events correlate perfectly with similar events recorded in the ice of Greenland. Both readings record these warming and cooling events on the same time frame. These two records indicate the end of the last Ice Age at about 14,800 years before the present. The Grey Scale (sediments) of the Caribbean indicates a warm period as warm as, or warmer, than now. This period lasted about 2,000 years. Then, abruptly about 12,800 years before present, the cold returned. This cold lasted for about 1,000 years or about 11,800 years before the present. This study attributes these events (the sediment layers) to high latitude North Atlantic sea surface temperatures.

Peter Ward, in his book, *The Call of Distant Mammoths*, makes some interesting statements: *"Dr. J. White of the Institute of Arctic and Alpine Research at the University of Colorado noted in a recent summary of the project that between 200,000 years ago and 10,000 years ago, average global temperature had changed as much as 18 degrees F in a few decades.... Dr. Minze Stuiver of the University of Washington has told me that such dramatic changes could have taken place in as little as five years. We have no experience of such a world; ... "* (6) p -199

Although I do not question the work of these scientists in interpreting the ice-cores of Greenland, I do not believe such a degree change can be attributed to the entire Earth just because it happened on Greenland. In fact, my intuition tells me, if the entire Earth changed that much in temperature, it would have caused a Global catastrophe in most of the major species groups of the time. I think it is more reasonable to assume the Greenland weather changed by possibly moving closer to the North Pole or being affected by major ocean current changes or air current changes.

The possible pole shift, as revealed in the previous uplift map, would surely have had such an effect on North Atlantic sea temperatures. The ocean currents certainly would have been different. The Equator would have crossed South America in the vicinity of Paraguay instead of Ecuador. The North Atlantic would still revolve in a similar fashion, but I believe there would have been less interaction with the South Atlantic.

Let us leave the physical evidence for a while and work with this new and rather accurate chronology of temperature in the North Atlantic region.

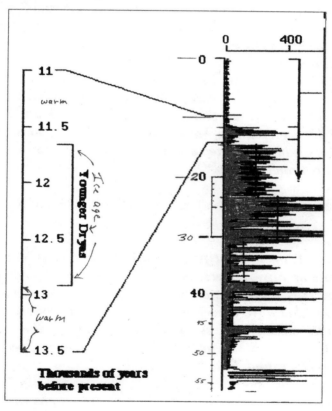

Graphic No. 23, Dust over Greenland, Chronology (21)

117

In our next section we will tie in the physical evidence of cultures that I believe developed and existed in that warm period from about 12,800 BC to about 10,800 BC. But first, let's see what Mr. "B" had to say about these pole movements and timing.

Mr. "B". On pole shifts

R: "In an article by a group from the University of Colorado and Harvard, I discovered a graph . . ." *B: "Yes."* R: " . . . of three abrupt changes in the weather in the Caribbean Sea. This was dated from records in the sediments. Are these correct?" *B: "Yes, very accurate."*

R: "Did the poles shift on these dates?" *B: "Yes."* R: "On all three dates?" *B: "Yes, and prior too."* R: "And what was the location before the last shift?" *B: "They go back and forth -- it was 18 degrees. You have to look at your world and your global markings, for they are not, . . . umm, . . . these are not 100% accurate, you see."*

R: "Can you give me the longitude and latitude before the last shift?"

B: "No. Your societal picture of your planet is not 100% accurate because, in fact, your planet is not a perfectly round sphere. It is somewhat elliptical, as you may be aware, and the grids that have been formed on this round sphere are not accurate, because it is not accurate. And the degrees longitude and latitude, or latitude, are not accurate because it is not really round."

(Obviously the errors we are willing to accept, as matters of fact seem to be too high to be acceptable at their level).

B: *"Let me assist you. If you took the pole (if the Earth was round), and moved it 18 degrees in a south southeast direction from magnetic north, you would be pretty accurate."*

R: "Magnetic north?" B: *"Yes, magnetic north."*

(Note) - The last pole location, as described by Mr. "B," is marked with a dot on the uplift map. This dot falls directly in the center of the effected area as described in the Geographical Bulletin. On the next move, will it return to this location? Some think it will.

R: "OK, What I've come up with, is there is a possibility that the two hundred outer miles of the Earth's crust can come loose and move around the center of the Earth. Is that correct?" B: *"That is what causes the movement of the Tectonic Plates."* R: "Well I mean actually deeper than the Tectonic plates." B: *"But that is actually what causes the movement of the Tectonic Plates, because one is going this way and one is going that way the actual core of the Earth. Do you understand?"* R: "Yes, does that turn normally the same as the spin of the Earth? (My question was unclear)." B: *"It runs in the opposite direction. Now you are talking about the outer crust."* R: "Yes." B: *"Yes, it is what's going to cause what we call the pole shift."* R: "The pole shift?" B: *"Yes."*

R: "Now there was an experiment in the book by John White called *Pole Shift*?" B: *"Yes."* R: "About mercury, the element. If you had a current in a fluid like mercury, it makes it firmer. Is that actually somewhat the trigger that makes it happen?" B: *"Umm, while the data is correct, it has little correlation to what actually occurs."*

R: "OK, so then it's not a change in the electron field which we plow through as the Earth plows through the electron field?" ***B: "Well it, umm, that does occur, but that is not the causative factor. Remember, I told you it was much greater."*** R: "Yes, it was galactic, you said." ***B: "Yes."*** R: "Like a galactic wave?" ***B: "Yes."*** R: "And does that wave have a variation of positive and negative?" ***B: "Oh, Indeed"***

R: "And when we cut through that wave, is that what changes the North and South Poles?" ***B: "Yes, magnetically."*** R: "Magnetically, yes, it doesn't spin. It just changes it magnetically, and during the null point when we move through that . . ."*** B: *"In that non-time. Because when you slice through or push through or however you . . . whatever time you . . . there is going to be a period of time or a period where time, as you understand it to be, does not exist. I see I have created great confusion."*** R: (laugh) ***B: "Disregard, but it is a fact that when . . . If you have two opposing magnets, they are going to repel. Do you understand?"*** R: "Yes, Two North Poles reject each other."

B: "Yes, if these two are as strong as what is going to occur, everything in that path is going to be repelled, and it's going to just stop. Do you understand? It is like a vacuum. Now it will not be a continuum, because you are moving through it. But, when these opposing magnetic fields come into alignment because of a galactic wave, which embraces far more than you can comprehend at this point in time. It is like it doesn't exist, and all things exist, simultaneously. It is a non-time."

R: "In the third dimension, how will that come across to us?" ***B: " Let me give you something you can comprehend. Do you recall reading historical data of how villages and animals and plant life were engulfed by great glaciers and in just a time*** *capsule of ice?* R: "Yes." **B: "That's how it affects this planet. All things are like in suspended animation. And whether it is one nanosecond or a million years, it is all the same. Do you understand this I speak?** R: "Not really." **B: "In your suspended animation, if you are in a non-time, suspended animation, you understand? Time does not exist. So, if it is a nanosecond or a million years, it is all the same.** R: "That's true, I can understand that."

B: "That is how entire villages, (and) entire populations of villages can be encapsulated in a time-capsule of ice. Because they and all things that surround them were in a time of suspended animation. How can you logically explain a living, breathing life form like a human or an animal, a mammoth or a deer, would stand still and allow themselves to be frozen and covered with ice. That is what occurs."

B: "Well now that I have thoroughly confused you, do you have further questions?"

This shocking information answered some questions and opened up a whole new bunch of others. So this is how a mammoth could be suffocated and frozen to death sitting up with flowers in his mouth. This is why some place on Earth, trees and broken bones were all piled up as if they were hit by a tidal wave. They probably were. My next question, of course, should have been, "Would we cease to exist when we go into suspended animation, or simply not remember?" But these questions were beyond my immediate comprehension. I was too taken aback to know what to ask. I only mention them here in the review of the physical truth and theoretical realities because later in the book we will bring out these same areas of discussion in the effects on humanity section. The point to accept here is this: Although we do not understand much of these theoretical happenings, we are not without some physical evidence of them in our human history.

Some species have been known to disappear totally during the pole switch period. Others have been encapsulated in ice in a way that we do not understand. This is powerful evidence that as life forms of Earth that live based on the rules of Earth's existence, we must operate within these rules, even if we do not understand them.

Three more questions

R: "I would just like to have some descriptions of the concept we call *no-time*. When people on Earth pass into this *no-time*, do they actually have a physical form, or are they kind of in a thought form?" *B: "There is going to be both."* R: "So there still is a physical reality?"

B: "There is a physical reality, but not anything you can equate it to in present time, and I could give you descriptions, but you still could not relate it to anything, and that's how humanity gleans information . . . by relating one bit of information to something similar in their bank of experience, you see."

R: "There's one question yet in my mind. When the pole adjustment takes place, then, does it (the physical part), take place in that period of *no-time*?" *B: "Yes."* R: "OK." So when people wake up, the change will already have happened?" *B: "That's correct."*

R: "In the Philadelphia Experiment, (the time traveling naval ship) some men were fused into the steel of the ship." *B: "Yes."* R: "Was this because they lost their focus?" *B: "And fear."* R: "And fear." *B: "It was a very frightening experience for most who participated, and the fear took control."* R: "If a person would have been able to not be afraid, would that have been helpful?" *B: "Oh, Indeed."* R: "How many survived that—did a lot survive?" *B: "Quite a number, yes, and not all survived in the same dimension."* R: "Yes, did one person actually survive in a later period of time?" *B: "Indeed."* R: "In the movie (*The Philadelphia Experiment*) that's about this subject. Is that fairly accurate then?" *B: "Yes, it is."* R: "Is there a book on that?" *B: "We perceive there is. It may not be in publication."* R: "I looked and couldn't find it."

We will end this discussion of the magnetic field here and bring it up later in the book.

7   Evidence of Ancient Cultures

There is now little doubt that cataclysmic weather events have affected mankind greatly in the past. However, it is more controversial to say that man had attained a high level of civilization before these events. Graham Hancock and others have undertaken the task of proving this. His book, *Finger Prints Of The Gods*, is a must read on this subject. It is only essential to the premise of this book to show the reader that there was a high probability that this actually did happen. I will start with the most highly published item in the controversy, the Sphinx.

Ancient Artifacts of Africa

The Sphinx: Hancock and West have both covered this very well. It is true, at this time; they cannot date this great monument precisely. Yet, they can with impunity prove that it is much older than the time of Pharaoh Khufu the one the Egyptologists tell us built it. They both imply it was in all probability built before the heavy rains and final flood at the end of the last ice age about 9,600 BC.

The Sphinx was probably built during the Golden Age of agriculture that occurred between 12,800 BC and 10,800 BC. This seemed to be the first real agriculture in Egypt.

".... Evidence unearthed since the 1970s by geologists, archaeologists and pre-historians like Michael Hoffman, Fekri Hassan and Professor Fred Wendorff has confirmed that the eleventh millennium BC was indeed an important period in Egyptian prehistory, and during which immense devastating floods swept down the Nile Valley (3). Rekri Hassan has speculated that this prolonged series of natural disasters, which reached a crescendo around or just after 10,500 BC (and continued

to recur periodically until about 9,000 BC) might have been responsible for snuffing out the early agriculture experiment (4)." (12) p - 412

It is also this rain that many believe did the very heavy water erosion on the Sphinx described by West in his tapes and book and pictured in Hancock's book. I am not going to explain the erosion further here. I will just say the Sphinx and the adjoining Valley Temple, and some times called the Temple of The Sphinx, are solid proof that there was an earlier civilized culture in Egypt. Also good evidence puts this culture in the 12,800 BC to 10,800 BC period. I believe it will soon be proven that this is an absolute truth. This will probably be done with the new magnetic rock alignment test now available.

One piece of astronomical evidence is the alignment of the Sphinx as an equinox marker during the Leo portion of the progression of the equinox cycle. This occurred at a time of about 10,500 BC. This may not seem as hard evidence, but when correlated with questions brought forward by the myths and cycles, its importance will become evident.

The Great Pyramid: The Great Pyramid and its two smaller sisters also exhibit a skill of monolithic masonry and astronomical and mathematical skill that is out of place in the chronology of the Egyptian history, as we know it. This has been discussed in numerous of books on the subject. They all basically say the same thing. There are no other items in the Egyptian architecture of the time, 2,500 BC - 1,000 BC, that directly compares to them. I will only say here, that they could better be explained if we had an earlier culture skilled in the art of stone construction beyond the current skills of today, and if that culture had the same understanding of the solar system we have today.

The arrangement of the three pyramids above on the same alignment as the star group known as Orion's Belt is just one of these implied skills.

Hypogeum: The last Egyptian physical monument I will introduce is the Hypogeum or Osireion. This little-discussed ancient Egyptian artifact located behind the Seti 1 Temple at Abydos, Egypt was also constructed with a monolithic construction style, little understood, and related to the Sphinx. One of its huge granite stones is over twenty-five feet long. It is best described by Murry and quoted by Hancock who visited the site.

"'This hypogeum,' wrote Margaret Murry, 'appears to Professor Petrie to be the place that Strabo mentions, usually called Strabo's Well' (12). This was good guesswork on the part of Petrie and Murray." (12) p - 399

After a superb description of this old building on which he quotes many of the former investigators, Hancock sums up this way:

"In a debate which many connections with that surrounding the Sphinx and the Valley Temple at Giza, eminent archaeologists had initially argued that the Osireion was a building of truly immense antiquity, a view expressed by Professor Naville in The London Times of March 1914:"

"This monument raises several important questions. As to its date, its great similarity with the Temple of the Sphinx [as the Valley Temple was then known] shows it to be of the same epoch when building was made with enormous stones without any ornament. This is characteristic of the oldest architecture in Egypt. I *should even say that we might call it the most ancient stone building in Egypt. (20)"* (12) p – 404

Graphic No. 24, Graham Hancock in Hypogeum,
Courtesy of Graham Hancock, (12) Plate 64

Ancient Egyptian Technology: We have mentioned here three things I would like to discuss in more detail. These items will be considered as indicating levels of technology in Egypt during the warm period before the last Ice Age. It can be thought of as 14,800 - 12,800 years before the present. It may help to say this is 12,800 - 10,800 years BC. I know in the mind of many, this point has not yet been proven, but I think you can see we are starting to make the case.

This technology, one that we cannot really say we can duplicate today, is the construction with enormous stones. These stones can often be over twenty feet long and six to ten feet thick or high and weighing 120 tons. Many times these stones are raised to positions very high in the structures. Often, they are cut to extreme tolerances, greater then we would even do today. Many, who want to believe the old myth of our 'ignorant' ancestors, try to do these feats usually with near

127

catastrophic results. Logic tells us these people used these stones in normal construction. I, for one, believe this represents a lost technology.

The second technology that represents relatively new information is the discovery of an agricultural-based society in the Nile Valley before the cold Younger Dryas period. Although unchallenged as far as I know, this does open up new perspectives.

The astronomical knowledge, thought to be available and used by the ancient Egyptians, astounds some of our well-qualified astronomers and mathematicians. This is the last point of discussion. The progression of the equinox, the star paths, the math concept of pi and the shape of the Earth are all concepts, that Stone Age cultures were not supposed to possess. How can this be explained within the current context of history? Well, we are not going to explain it here, either. We just want you to be open to the same questions we have. Let's go on to look at all of the data before we jump to any conclusions.

Ancient artifacts of South America

To some it will come as a surprise that anyone considers any of the archeological sites of the Americas as ancient or, at least, in the same league as the Sphinx and the Pyramids. Well, you need to hear about Professor Arthur Posnansky and Professor Rolf Muller.

The city of Tiahuanaco: Near the famous lake, Titicaca on the border of Bolivia and Peru, there is an old stone city called Tiahuanaco. This city, once a port on the lake, has a large stone pier to prove it. One stone in the pier was estimated at 440 tons and many others at 100 to 150 tons. There are many other unusual features in this city that need to be brought to light here.

"The orthodox historical view is that the ruins cannot possibly be dated much earlier than AD 500 (11). An alternative chronology also exists, however, which, although not accepted by the majority of scholars, seems more in tune with the scale of the geological upheavals that have occurred in this region. Based on mathematical/astronomical calculations of Professor Arthur Posnansky of the University of La Paz, and of Professor Rolf Muller (who also challenged the official dating of Machu Picchu), it pushes the main phase of construction at Tiahuanaco back to 15,000 BC. This chronology also indicates that the city suffered immense destruction in a phenomenal natural catastrophe around the eleventh millennium BC, and thereafter rapidly became separated from the lakeshore. (12) " (12) p - 66.

What actually have these local investigators found that have led them to this unusual conclusion? There is no question that this city was once a port, even though now it is more than 12 miles from the lake. There is an immense dock that would have held numerous ships. Hancock quoted historian Garcilaso De La Vega of the sixteenth century to describe it,

"There is an artificial hill, of great height, built on stone ... these are much worn which shows their great antiquity. There are walls, the stones of which are so enormous it is difficult to what human force could have put them in place. And there are the remains of strange buildings, the most remarkable being stone portals, hewn out of solid rock; these stand on bases anything up to 30 feet long, 15 feet wide and 6 feet thick, base and portal being all of one piece ... How, and with what tools or implements, massive works of such size could be

achieved are questions which we are unable to answer ... Nor can it be imagined how such enormous stones could have been brought here... (3)" (12) p - 72 & 73.

Above: 13 Tiahuanaco's Gateway of the Sun, viewed from the west. It is carved out of a single piece of solid andesite and weighs more than 10 tons.

Graphic No. 25, Gate Way of The Sun
Courtesy of Graham Hancock, (12) Plate 13

One part, called the *Gateway of the Sun*, needs special mention here, because it possesses more than the massive stone technology we have come to expect. It may, also, have ancient solar alignments. This portal has carvings of extinct elephants and toxodons (a larger rhino/hippo-like creature). These animals died out here about 10,000 to 12,000 years ago.

We should also be aware that strong physical evidence of massive catastrophe is still at the site. Many of the huge stones were thrown out of place and remain so today. No geological history in the recent few thousand years can explain these artifacts.

If any one has questions, they should review Posnansky's book, *Tiahuanaco: The Cradle of American Man.* This book represents almost fifty years of work and must be taken seriously. Other scientists have reviewed this work more recently and have concluded it is basically correct.

One last quote is of major importance to our question of weather.

"At the same time [after the catastrophe] there was evidence that the climate of the Tiahuanaco area had become colder and much less favorable for the growing of crops than had previously been the case, (13) so much less favorable that today staples such as maize cannot ripen properly and even potatoes come out of the ground stunted." (12) p - 90

There is much more that could be said of this interesting site, but we need to move on to the well-known mountaintop site of Machu Picchu.

Machu Picchu: Here we will only mention two things: First, the same monolithic stonework exists that is so typical of the construction of the much earlier period 12,800 plus years ago. Second, the place does not seem to have weather favorable to what would be the expected use. Although this alone is not enough to re-date the site, I believe the site can better be explained within the context of the much earlier period. For that reason, I would like to see the large base stones dated with the magnetic stone placement process. If this is done, I believe it will prove the site predates the end of the last glacier period, just like the other sites using this technology. Later in the book, I will explain why I think the weather was different at the earlier period.

Micronesia, Islands of Pohnpei: There is one last piece of physical evidence I would like to mention. My only reference is from a television special I saw in 1999. It described a large bunch of stonework's on small islands in the area of the island of Pohnpei in the western Pacific Ocean. It appears that some culture attempted to raise several of the islands in a desperate attempt to stay above a gradual rising of the ocean level. The massive stonework incorporated some very large stones, some 50 tons, fit into the construction concept of our ancient stone workers. The creators of the program estimated possibly 145 million tons of stone were placed.

The current culture does not seem to be able to support that level of effort. The local natives state the ancients somehow levitated the stones into place. These two pieces of information, plus the fact the last major sea level change was when the last glaciers were melting 14,800 years ago, or more likely 15,000 plus years ago, indicate a not-yet described culture.

The current local natives said an ancient people levitated the stones into place. If we go into the more esoteric information, we may consider the Atlantian or Lamurian cultures of legend. I decided to ask my spirit guide about this location, since I had no way to check it out within the scientific arena. He confirmed the site was what we can think of as the Lamurian culture of old.

This completes our look for physical evidence of the ancient civilized peoples. I think you can see that if we open our eyes, we will see much more. These artifacts, of this broad civilization, have been right in front of us all the time. New technologies of dating will point out many more, I am sure. But, for now we will move to myth and legend, not for proof, but to describe the cataclysms that befell these people and to show how they probably happened. We will blend the myths and three actual dates taken from undersea chronological charts. These will explain the physical evidence brought out above.

I decided to ask Mr. "B" about these dates.

R: "One period was shown as a warm period about 12,800 BC to 10,800 BC. Was that when the Sphinx and the great Pyramid were built?" *B: "Umm... In that... It's fairly close."*

R: "I did some work that a ½ glacial cycle was 10.800 years (question implied)?" *B: "That's not exact. It's longer than that."*

R: "That's what I thought because it doesn't fit the recent data." *B: "Yes, that's not an accurate... More about 13,500 to 15,000 years."*

R: "Is the original stone work in South America at Lake Titicaca and Machu Picchu of the (pre) glacial time?" *B: "Some is, some isn't."* R: "What about Machu Picchu itself?" *B: "That would be back at the time the Pyramids and the Sphinx were in construction. When you get your graph completed, you will see that very clearly."*

R: "Can you tell me how the stone was cut and placed?" *B: "A process you have no experience to understand. They used vibration. Vibration creates sound, but it was the actual vibration that was the mechanism."*

R: "The high mountain city of Machu Picchu is cold and fore-boding" (interrupted). *B: "It was very hospitable."* R: "Was it because it was lower, or was it because it was at a different location of latitude?" *B: "Both."*

R: "I saw a special on TV about the Island of Pohnpei in Micronesia," . . . *B: "Yes"* R: . . . "and it described the ancient stone works. These were . . . They had attempted to raise the islands. Do these go way back?" *B: "Lemuria."* R: "OK. That is Lemuria. Would that have been about 15,000 years ago when the Glaciers were melting or is it older?" *B: "It's older."* R: "Can you tell me about. . ." *B: "About Lemuria?"* R: " . . . what they found now? Is there something specific there?"

B: "I don't perceive they know what they found, as yet. Lemuria was a multi-cultured existence, and they were . . . It wasn't a class system. Each group of individuals had specific tasks to perform, and no task was more important than another. It was simply a utopian way of life. They had scholars, but the scholars were no more revered than the stone masons, and the stone mason was no more revered than the spiritual teacher, and it was a very compatible and homo—static society. They contributed great art, music, literary works, healing mechanisms, industrial mechanisms; all sorts of things came as a result of that culture. But, because it was so ancient, most individuals do not have consciousness memory of having an association with that culture. Do you understand?" R: "Yes."

R: "That's one of my questions. Did I ever live there?" *B: "No, but you had ties to there through your ancestry just as most individuals did."*

R: "Where would they have gone from there? What cultures do we have now that are direct descendants?"

B: "I don't believe there are any direct descendants, umm, of Lemurians, but probable the closest that you are going to find, that endeavored to carry out that system, and it greatly failed, is the people like India, Pakistan, that area, with their class system. But it was not a class or caste system of (in) Lemuria. Do you understand?"

R: "Yes, it was just a system based on respect." *B: "and function. It takes the whole."* R: "Shared goals?" *B: "Yes."*

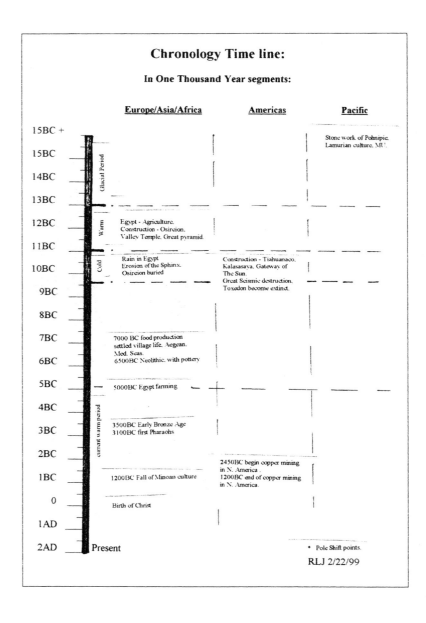

Chronology Time line:

In One Thousand Year segments:

Europe/Asia/Africa	Americas	Pacific

15BC +

Glacial Period

Stone work of Pohnpie,
Lamurian culture. MU.

15BC

14BC

13BC

12BC — Egypt - Agriculture.
Construction - Osireion,
Valley Temple, Great pyramid.

Warm

11BC

10BC — Rain in Egypt
Erosion of the Sphinx.
Osireion buried

Cold

Construction - Tiahuanaco,
Kalasasaya, Gateway of
The Sun.

9BC — Great Seismic destruction,
Toxodon become extinct.

8BC

7BC — 7000 BC food production
settled village life. Aegean.
Med. Seas.

6BC — 6500BC Neolithic, with pottery

5BC — 5000BC Egypt farming

4BC

current warm period

3BC — 3500BC Early Bronze Age
3100BC first Pharaohs

2BC — 2450BC begin copper mining
in N. America .

1BC — 1200BC Fall of Minoan culture
1200BC end of copper mining
in N. America.

0 — Birth of Christ

1AD

2AD — Present

• Pole Shift points.

RLJ 2/22/99

8   Myths of the Ancient Past

I am going to select only a few myths since a whole book could be written on these creation stories as they are often called. I think it is helpful to stop here and rename these myths. It seems much more accurate to me to call them verbal histories or verbal recollections, much the same as we tell about the good old times or the bad old times, whichever leaves the most traumatic effect on us. I also want to focus on stories that mention cataclysmic or weather-related phenomenon.

Who lived through the last Earth change?

Well, of course, the ancestors of all of us lived through it. But, who exhibited traits that might lead us to believe that they lived through it and remembered the crisis?

Mesopotamia: The first story we all know very well. It's from the Christian Bible, the story of Noah and the ark. As we remember, it tells of numerous days of rain, forty to be exact. However, exact is probably not what was meant here. Anyway, there was two of each animal, etc. Well, you remember.

The second story, closely related, was the legend of Gilgamesh. He was a Sumerian person from the same area. It probably was recorded earlier than the Noah story, but was most likely, just another tribal memory of the same type of event. If the Hebrews and the Sumerians had common ancestry, it may even be the same story, but I don't think we have enough information to say about that either way.

Did these people act as if they had observed an Earth change? Well, yes, they did in many ways. First, they built the large mountain-like Ziggurat, the Tower of Babel, and devel-

137

oped a very extensive system of solar observation platforms. They worshipped the sun and other solar bodies. These actions could have been related to such a trauma.

In the same general area, Hancock tells us about some other early people. This is the Avestic Aryans of Pre-Islamic Iran. Their story is similar to the first two; however, there is one big difference. Instead of forty days of rain, they get very heavy snowfall. They describe it this way in their ancient writings:

> *"Then Angra Mainyu, who is full of death, created an opposition to the same, a mighty serpent and snow. Ten months of winter are there now, two months of summer, and these are as cold as the water, cold as to the Earth, cold as to trees ... There all around falls deep snow; that is the direst of plagues... "* (2), (12) p - 201.

Now, I don't think we should think of this as Iran. The common belief is that the origin of these people lies further to the north, probably somewhere on the Steppes in Russia.

These people were also warned and told to make underground enclosures for themselves, all the animals, birds, and succulent plants. They were told to bring in the red burning fires (heat) and flowing water (to drink). They were warned not to bring any deformed or infertile animals. It was obvious that these were to be a breeding population, not something they planned to eat in their underground caves. It was known by someone that animals left above ground would be killed or frozen to death. This event probably took place during the last Earth change.

People of the Lion Gate (the Sphinx), Pre-Glacial Period Egyptians: In Egypt, we have enough history and legends to write several books. We will only mention a few here. We have recorded, by the Greek historian Diodorus, information given to him by the Heliopolitan priests. This seems to be a good place to start.

> *"In general, they say that if in the flood which occurred in the time of Deucalion"* (the Greek Noah), *"most living things were destroyed, it is probable that the inhabitants of southern Egypt survived rather than any others ... Or if, as some maintain, the destruction of living things was complete and the Earth brought forth again new forms of animals, never the less, even on such a supposition, the first genesis of living things fittingly attaches to this country ... (5)"* (12) p - 388.

Of course, we know now, all the animals were not killed off with the Earth putting out new ones. But this must have been what it seemed like to any people who were around when sixty genera of species went extinct and other smaller ones took their place. Hancock makes a few observations that are very appropriate here.

> *"Why should Egypt have been so blessed? Diodorous was told that it had to do with geographical situation, with the great exposure of its southern regions to the heat of the sun, and with the vastly increased rainfall which the myths said the world had experienced in the aftermath of the universal deluge: 'For when the moisture from the abundant rains which fell among other peoples was mingled with the intense heat which prevails in Egypt itself ... the air becomes very well tempered for the first generation of all living things ... (6)"* (12) p - 388 & 389

Let's talk of how it might have been. There may have been a people who lived on the Nile and the eastern Mediterranean.

139

They were quite advanced both spiritually and as the last Earth changes approached, technologically (they had built the Pyramids and The Sphinx). The shamans were allowed to see what was about to happen. When the time came, they were told to go hide in the caves. Some did this when the changes came. They survived because of this closeness with spirit.

After the changes, the southern Nile Valley, in Egypt, became a very good place to live for the cold rainy time. However, when the warm weather came back, this area turned back into a desert place. This is probably when they discovered the copper oxide that helped them to cope with the suns rays. They had to bore new caves and tried to adapt to the hot dry weather. This would only have been for a few years; then they would have migrated to a better place to live.

I believe many of these people were from an area along the southwest shores of the Red Sea, where the pearl beds and clams were prevalent. Clams may well be a food source that can survive the changes. Now, we know this area as the Sudan and Ethiopian shores of the Red Sea. There may be a connection to the clams and pearls that stick with the survivors for millennia. The Algonquin still talk about the arm reaching out of the sea holding a shell. This may have been a pictograph for an area with a food supply. Foods that are used in very harsh times can become sacred.

Fish might, and probably, will relocate due to the weather changes and current changes in the oceans. Large numbers of four-legged animals may well be killed off, but the clams could deal with the tsunamis, the silt, and the forces and still survive.

Now, back to real evidence. The weathering controversy with the Sphinx that we pointed out earlier now seems to find a suitable context. The acceptance of water erosion on it puts its origin back to before 9,700 BC, the time of the heavy rains and floods during the end of the Ice Age. These people, if they had built such monuments and temples, must have had a significantly civilized culture, skilled in many ways we can only dream of. Legend and archaeology, alike, both seem to indicate they may be survivors of a much more advanced civilization group.

In my last book, I was clearly able to document that many technologies and copper and other metal work appear to have developed in the eastern Mediterranean region. A large number of seeds, foods, and animal husbandry developed there, also. But, maybe it did not really develop there. It just may have been remembered there. After all, now we know that there was an agricultural period thousands of years earlier in Egypt. What else don't we know of this warm spell over ten thousand years ago, simply because we haven't looked?

These people also seemed to worry about the sun's fidelity to its track in the sky. They named each of the movable sky objects. In Egypt, they built the temple of Carnac to track the movement of the sun. They built some more of the pyramids.

We don't really know why the first Great pyramid and two smaller ones were built, but some say they are connected with the stars on the belt of Orion; others say they are part of a great initiation. I believe these are from the ancient culture. We do not understand the technology and can only speculate at the reason for construction.

Paraguay, Argentina and Chile: Not all parts of the Earth faired so well as Egypt. We will now go back to the creation stories of South America. The Toba Indians of this area still repeat this myth.

"Asin told a man to gather as much wood as he could and to cover his hut with as thick a layer of thatch, because a time of great cold was coming. As soon as the hut had been prepared Asin and the man shut themselves inside and waited. When the great cold set in, shivering people arrived to beg a firebrand from them. Asin was

hard and gave embers only to those who had been friends. The people were freezing, and they cried the whole night. At midnight they were all dead, young and old, men and women ... this period of ice sleet lasted for a long time and all the fires were put out. Frost was as thick as leather. (8) " (12) p - 202

This would have been at the end of the last Ice Age when the last pole shift took place about 9,800 BC. The Equator moved approximately 2,000 miles north where it crosses South America.

What of the Hopi Legend: The Hopi claim to be the first people of North America, and I have no reason to doubt the reasons for this claim. But I would suggest they were the first after the last shift. In fact, I believe that their myths and legends support this very well, especially the migration story and the predictions that we are recently hearing so much about.

The migration story is key here. If the shift we are suggesting happened 11,800 years ago, and Siberia moved roughly 2,000 miles closer to the North Pole, the hunting and weather conditions would have substantially worsened.

The surviving Siberian people would have needed to migrate. Not only would they have needed to migrate, they would actually be looking for the most optimum place to live. In fact, this is what the Hopi migration myth suggests, a people, no longer sure of where the best place to live is. In their verbal histories, they indicate exploring a new land, presumably without people if they believed they were the first. They journeyed to the east coast, and west coast, and then all the way to the southern tip of South America before finally setting in their homeland in the North American southwest. This could well describe a continent recently devoid of most of its people by a cataclysmic pole shift.

The predictions we are hearing today, made thousands of years ago by their ancestors, would also come from an awareness of the disaster and the close connection with the spirit necessary to survive it.

French Cave Artists: I will call them the French cave artists of 17,000 BC. Apparently, they had adjusted to the southern edge of the European glacial ice, hunting the Ice-Age mammals that lived in that zone. I really don't know what happened to them. As the ice receded, I assume they adjusted to the other animal populations and survived by hunting them. Their world was to improve. The new ocean currents would warm the land. The animals, though smaller, were abundant. They could move out of the deep caves and live again on the surface.

But, did they remember these traumatic changes? Someone started building massive stone monuments. Was this to track the "Errant Sun?" Stonehenge and New Grange could have been an attempt to record and keep track of this potential problem instead of just the annual growing seasons. They started saying prayers to make sure the sun came up and went down on a regular schedule. Were these the actions of a people who were traumatized by the movement of the Sun from its normal patterns? Why else would they be concerned if they had not, at one time in the distant past, been affected by it.

Human history is full of these legends. It seems nowhere on Earth did man's life progress without these catastrophic changes. The evidence, it seems, is always there if only we can ask the right questions. I believe it is now time to listen to these whispers from the past and our prophets' warnings. What have we to lose if we look? We may have much to lose if we fail to look.

I asked Mr. "B" about these legends

R: "The Sumerian people appeared to be survivors of these cataclysmic changes. Can you tell me where they survived?"
B: "In caves, some in valleys, they were in little—What do you call it?—bands tribes, groups."

R: "Were they in Africa or in the Middle East?" *B: "No, they were definitely in the Middle Eastern part at this time."*

R: "Were there other locations where people survived?" *B: "Certainly."*

R: "How about in North America?" *B:* (There were)*"A great number of places in this North American Continent where individuals survived."*

(This question refers to why people in the myths appear to see the sun move. How could they do this if they were in suspended animation?)

R: "I am confused then. In some of the myths, the people seem to have seen the erratic movements of the sun. I thought they were supposed to be in suspended animation?"

B: "You must understand, umm, eons past up through the last 3-400 years, any time a comet, particularly the ones closer and more visible such as Haley's, comes into the visible perspective of inhabitants, they could not or didn't chose to understand what was occurring. Now there are accounts of great meteorite showers. If you could remove all your flora from your planet, and it be much as barren as your moon, you would see that it has many more crater impacts than your moon does and a lot of other planets, as far as that is concerned. So, there have been periods of time of great meteorites plummeting to your Earth in great showers. So yes, those myths are both, umm, lack understanding and are a reality."

R: "They were not in suspended animation then?"

B: "No, it was not what they perceived when certain comets passed; it was that they inherently knew that it had occurred. They did not visually see it, but when these comets passed fairly close, they interpreted that, as that was what was occurring. Do you understand?" R: "I think so." *B: "Just as you know that this has occurred, you haven't visually seen it, but you know. So, if you saw comets very close, you might interpret it that this was falling from the sky."*

This is what I think he was saying. The people were in suspended animation at the time of the pole shift, but they did see some of the preliminaries. The also knew there was a shift, but when they put it together, they didn't know what they were seeing. This makes it unclear in their myths.

R: "On November 17 & 18, 2031, we are going to get a sign from the comet Temple Tuttle." *B: "Yes."* R: "Will that be like normal shooting stars, or will there be a lot of pieces big enough to go all the way to the ground?" *B: "There will be sizable pieces that will reach the surface of your planet."* R: "When they come all the way down, they make a big mark in the sky. They will be more impressive." *B: "Yes."* R: "It seems like it must have happened when the natives wrote about it." *B: "Yes, when the stars fell they state."*

3/26/98 - R: "The night before last, my friend saw a program on sarcophagi from Crete, Egypt, Turkey and Greece. She wanted to know if these were the same people I've been

145

writing about in my book *Ancient Mines of Kitchi-Gummi*?"
B: "Yes."

R: "She would like you to tell us something about the mining process that produced this."

B: "Well, it was extracts of ore that were mined deep within the Earth. There are, to this present time, deposits of copper in that part of the world. It is because of the oxidation of that product that the river called Nile is green. People of that region of the world were desert-type dwellers. (It was) *very hot, very dry, and they originally discovered this by endeavoring to dig deep in the Earth to build shelters, and they used implements that could astound the present day world, innovative Archemedial-type digging implements. They were unaware of the value or the potential of this ore, but they were intrigued because of its coloration and the striations within the ore. As they were digging and building themselves tunnels and endeavoring to make shelters, they would use papyrus reeds to line the tunnels. But as they were putting those in place, the copper ore would slough off—you know the term, slough off—and get upon their bodies, their hands, and their faces. And they soon discovered it had reflective properties, and it made their bodies cooler. And it did not parch their skin, because copper is a mineral. It has an oily-type consistency to it when it is powdered or sloughed, and they used it for ointment for many years, a long period of time. But as this began to become more familiar to a large number of people, they used it for trading, and they used it for various implements. But their primary use was to grind it with great wheels of stone that had been quarried many miles away, and use it to cover their bodies to reflect the sun's rays.*

Because in a desert-type environment, the sun is triply intensified because of the color of the sand—it is like being in

146

an oven. So that is how that primarily came about, but, of course, as time went on, the people became more nomadic, and they journeyed great distances, even to this continent, and brought this technology and usage with them, and through time, progressed to the uses of this mineral called copper in its present state."

What next? If anything I've theorized so far is true, I would say the following actions may prove to be prudent. First, the glacial weather patterns and the progression the equinox cycle must be studied extensively. Astronomers must see if they can find a galactic wave that our solar system is passing through. Maybe one of these could explain the time frames.

Second, those who study the Earth's magnetic fields both past and present should see if it can be related to some unknown galactic cycle. This cycle should be carefully studied and the levels of magnetic field around the Earth must be carefully monitored. I would recommend geophysicist should investigate the trigger theory known as Magnetohydrodynamic Energy. The people who know the past weather history on a planet-wide scale should study and model what the weather is. They should study what ocean and atmospheric currents were around 18,000 years ago, and what they would be now if we were to return to that general pole location indicated by Mr. B.

Someone should be pulling it all together and develop, at least, three probabilities that could answer the facts as we perceive them to be. The probable scenarios should be modeled and tested on some good computer systems. Governments, world wide, should make plans accordingly to the scenarios and suggestions. Safe zones should be located and small contingency governments should be set up at the proper time. They should be equipped with long-band radio systems that could transmit around the world on AM bands. All satellite communication will be disrupted as well as landline systems.

The dust will be heavier in the Northern Hemisphere due to the concentrations of land surfaces there. The pivot point for the adjustment will be in Africa. This is well to remember. This is why the species diversity is so high there. Not as many species are affected by the changes.

A person could write a whole book on survival, but that is not the purpose of this book. I have only included the items above to indicate we must think and become aware. This is the route to human survival. I will leave this now and move into a new area, Part Four. Humanity: What roll do we play in this grand era?

9   What We Humans Are

Humanity and Magnetism

To begin to understand the concept of N*o-time* and no electromagnetic field, I began reading two authors who were already addressing this issue, Greg Braden and Barbara Brennen. Both of these writers have studied this subject for many years: Greg from the point of the solar system, and Barbara from the point of the human body. Lucky for me, they both address the lesser and greater levels of consciousness at the same time. This helped me to put their work in a holographic context. I needed their work to start making sense of the information I was uncovering. With it, I was able to begin addressing some of my own questions.

If we are truly magnetic beings in the third dimension, and we are totally unable to function when we are not in an electromagnetic field, then maybe, we will not function uniformly in a variable magnetic field. We have long known about the effects of the full moon and how it makes people "crazy"—well, at least, a few people. Maybe this is the process that makes humanity's love affair with the Zodiac and the astrological charts so enduring. Earth stones record the magnetic print of the Earth's magnetic field as they are formed or crystallize. Maybe man records the Zodiac's energy pattern, in the same way, when he takes physical form.

As physical and electrical entities of this planet, we must follow the rules even if we don't understand them. At some point we must leave the great magnetic electron body-field of our mothers. When we do this, we move into an electronic field created and balanced by the major planetary beings of our solar system. At birth then, do we really form our physical energy print from the world we are born into, and do we use this inner magnetic reference throughout our whole life? This is an interesting point but further discussion here is not beneficial to the development of this part of man's story.

Early man and magnetism: When I was visiting the New England Antiquities Research Association Conference Meeting in New England in the spring of 1999, I became aware of the relationship between magnetic fields and stone chambers in that area. At the time, this was entirely new information that left me somewhat puzzled. What was this local interest all about? It wasn't long before the connections would become evident and important in my life.

It appears that native peoples of that area could sense changes in the Earth's electromagnetic field. The stone chambers were carefully placed to take advantage of dips in the magnetic field strength. We might say (Yin) places. The apparent reason for this was to be in a place where it was easier to receive messages from spirits, or visions as they were referred to then.

Here we have a premise for a theory, based on the concept that the ancients knew something we do not. Does the reduced level of the Earth's electromagnetic field make humanity more open to spirits? Or does it in some way make his sub consciousness, or God-consciousness more accessible? Is this the source principal for the importance of the concept of Yin and Yang?

Gregg Braden: It seems to follow, if our thoughts are a series of switches, that if we were in a strong electromagnetic field, these switches would be held in their position with more force. Yet if the electromagnetic field is weaker, maybe these switches could more easily be changed. I had held this idea as a possible truth when I discovered and read Gregg Braden's book, *Awakening to Zero Point.* He took this theory much further. To quote him is the best way to point out the concept.

In the section of his book labeled, "Magnetic Tension: The Glue of Consciousness," we find the following ideas:

"The energy referred to as consciousness is electromagnetic energy/information/light that is bound up within some aspect of the magnetic field of our planet. ... Please understand that it is the awareness of human kind, and not the life essence itself, that is used to interpret the three dimensional world, the self and ultimately the creator. ... It is this awareness that is locked up within the fields of magnetics surrounding the planet. Through the structure provided as fields of magnetics, the net of our awareness matrix is stabilized and secured in place." (14) p - 21.

"Energetically, we are electrical in nature. Each cell within each component of our body generates a charge of approximately 1.17 volts at a specific frequency for that organ." (14) p - 22.

"The magnetic fields surrounding each cell of your body may be thought of as a buffer stabilizing the information of the soul within each cell. This buffer creates "drag" or friction around each cell, effectively interfering with your ability to fully access that body of information. Earth's fields of magnetics have, historically, been your safety zone between thought and manifestation. Early in this cycle of consciousness, magnetics were high, providing a distance between the formulation of a thought and the consequences of that thought. ... Now, as the intensity of the fields decrease, the lag time between a thought, and the realization of that thought, is decreasing proportionally. Perhaps you have noticed how quickly you are able to manifest in your world."

"Lower magnetic fields provide the opportunity for change through rapid manifestation of thought and feeling." (14) p - 23.

Braden not only indicates the relationship between the Earth's magnetic fields and consciousness, but he goes on to indicate how the processes affect the speed of manifestation. A little later Braden talks of how the King's Chamber of the Great Pyramid was apparently designed and used to lower the effective magnetic field and aid in the training of temple initiates.

"The kings chamber of the great pyramid offers a very unique environment, the source of which remains a mystery to modern science. Within the tuned resonant cavity of the chamber of light, measurements of Earth's magnetics drop to nearly zero." (14) p - 37.

Some have suggested this may have been the function of the pyramid mass: to focus the Earth's magnetic field much as a magnifying glass focuses light. We all have seen the dark spot where light is removed by being focused elsewhere. Braden goes on to say:

"Earlier in this text, it was noted that in the presence of a relatively strong field of magnetics, a lag time is produced between thought and the crystallization of that thought. Additionally, it is within the buffers of dense magnetic fields that the interference patterns of emotions are stored holographically surrounding, as well as within, the body. The absence of magnetics provides the opportunity for direct access to the individual as pure information. It is within this environment, without the safety net of magnetics, that thought becomes very potent. Through the gift of this very pure environment, initiates, having mastered personality, ego, fear, judgment,

forgiveness and compassion simply begin to think. Possibly for the first time in life, the thoughts are their own and not the imprints of a consensus reality, or the constraints imposed upon them through conditioning. Through direct access to themselves, the initiates become "real." Within that reality, they carry themselves, beyond the limitations resulting from the life experiences." (14) p – 38

We will leave Braden's book here now. He also has produced a tape on the same subject. The questions below go into some of the ideas discussed on the tape. It's sufficient to say that he goes on in both the book and the tape to discuss his perceptions of the magnetic effects on mankind further; how the reducing and reversing Earth's magnetic field he envisions, will give the opportunity to a large number of individuals to complete a resurrection or a change of state. This process he believes the Egyptian initiates went through as well as possibly our great teacher, the Christ. If you are interested in further reading, this book is a good candidate.

Here are Mr. "B's" comments

R: "I bought three books in Madison, *Awakening to Zero Point*, by Gregg Braden (was one of them.)" **B: *"A very good book."***

R: "It seems accurate with regards to the magnetic effects on people, but it seems wrong on where the Earth's magnetic fields come from." ***B: " It's not accurate on that, but it's a good perspective on how it affects individuals."***

R: "OK, the Earth's magnetic field, the way I perceive it, is generated by a mass of the Earth moving through an electrical field. Is that true?" ***B: "That's correct."***

R: "What else is important to learn out of this book?" *B: "That's the most. It's magnetic effect on individuals."*

R: "I received and viewed a tape called *Awaking to Zero Point* (also by Braden). Is this fairly accurate?" *B: "Umm, it is, shall we say, mostly accurate."*

R: "In the discussion on human DNA, he says, "The human DNA entrains the photons." Is this true, and are they energized by emotion to do this?" *B: "Yes."* R: "Does the emotion wave open and close these little switches? Is that what's happening?" *B: "Yes."* R: "And then it imprints that on the light photons?" *B: "Correct."*

R: "Is this the same process that affects the photons we pass through between Jupiter and the Sun?" *B: "Almost exactly."* R: "Would we think of these being entrained by a consciousness of Jupiter or an intelligence of some sort?" *B: "Not necessarily of Jupiter, but a consciousness that is universal."* R: "OK. Would that be like God-Consciousness?" *B: "That is another way to understand it. Yes."*

R: "In this galactic wave, the one we are going to enter into with reverse polarity, is that the same thing? Is it caused by the same thing?" *B: "It is not caused, umm, by exactly the same thing, but it is the same thing. How can I explain this to you? It is the same thing, only in reverse, if you can comprehend this, I speak."* R: "So the photons are entrained; they're entrained backwards."

R: "Is this emotional energy a different energy than magnetism?" *B: "Yes."* R: "What would we use to measure this? Would that yin-yang be used to measure it?"

B: "Well, that is one measurement. Really, you don't have an accurate method in which to calculate the measurements that would be needed to find an equation, a mathematical equation, so you could comprehend this human emotion and its ... umm ... "dynamics."

R: "Is emotion a photon-based energy?" (Hesitation). *B: "In part."* R: "OK." *B: "For your purpose, yes."*

R: "Do we create our own emotions, or do we just filter the energy that comes from God's emotions?" *B: "No, God's emotions are pure, so the emotions of jealousy, anger, fear, hatred, lack, and desperation are created by humanity."* R: "So, we actually create those emotions. We don't just mess them up?" *B: "Correct."*

R: "Braden talked about the resonance pulse of the Earth, and how it was about 7.8, and now it's about 9 and rising and may go to 13. Is this correct?" *B: "It's quite possible with all that's going to occur."* R: "Does that have anything to do with the Jose Silva's stuff?" *B: "Yes, it does."* R: "He said it was like ten cycles per second. It's getting close to that?" *B: "Yes."*

R: "According to Braden, the ancients said this was going to take place between 1987-2012. Is this correct, or shouldn't I be asking the question?"

B: "You can certainly ask the question as you say. Umm. First of all we don't see that the ancients thought or stated this." R: "OK." *B: "Nextly, it could occur within that time frame, but I wouldn't, if I were on your plane of existence, I wouldn't do too much to prepare in that time frame."*

R: "Is the male/female energy an expression of a photon-based energy?" ***B: "Yes."***

R: "On a TV program they said the army has an electromagnetic pulse weapon that disrupts the electromagnetic field over a large area. How would this affect the people in there?" ***B: "Adversely, very adversely."*** R: "Like you told me one time, it could fry you." ***B: "Correct."***

Braden's book supports perfectly the concepts put forward by those from New England Antiquities Research Association in their Stone Chamber Studies. It also supports those who are saying the Earth changes have already begun, at least in the psyche of man. We will leave the concept of preparing to live in the fourth dimension to others. It is important to realize, to continue to live on this orb we call Earth, we will have to be able to experience the *No-time Zone* and survive. If this means we will have to be able to change our vibration level, I cannot say at this time.

I asked Mr. "B" for guidance on the subject

R: (I asked a rather vague question about thought energy. I didn't really know what I was talking about). He answered, ***"What is it you wish to know?"*** (I was still unprepared to elaborate, so he went on to explain the subject some.)

B: "You can create without awareness. Humanity does this moment by moment. Put more simply, let me begin even further back. The human brain is made up of millions of cells and each of those cells has an electrical component. It fires quite rapidly, and it creates energy. That's all it is, pure energy, until a thought, based upon instinctual knowledge that is innate in each and every human being or experiential knowledge. A thought begins to form. That thought has given

life to electrical mass. When I say mass, some individuals are seeing things this big, (Indicates about 12" size.) *but it's a pin point, and is propelled by electrical impulse, by human emotion, into another electrical field which is the stuff which is all around you and the universe. Energy, as you are aware, cannot be destroyed. It can be changed, it can be harnessed, it can be diverted, but it cannot be destroyed.* (This) *collective electrical mass, when enough individuals have created a similar molecular thought pattern, they bond together because they have similar structure. That creates matter, and matter creates living forms. In the way your world works, in society, in the flora and the fauna, everything in the entire universe and all other universes are created in the same manner."*

"Now, just let's assume for a moment that ten thousand people are gathered, and they are all focused on the same thing. That is a lot of energy, and when that energy goes out into the universe and molecularly bonds with other energies that have been projected out over eons of time, you have the beginnings of new paradigms. And it's quite complex, but when humanity has reached the apex of awareness, or when humanity's thoughts can be of the purest intent, great and miraculous things can occur. But in your world that has not occurred yet, but it is not an impossibility. Human emotions are so important very few individuals understand the finite principal of the human emotion."

R: "Emotion is then another type of energy?" *B: "Oh, Indeed!"* R: "It's separate from this?" (Implying thought energy). *B: "Another matter, Yes. An analogy would be, you could build the most exquisite spacecraft, have the most sophisticated engines, but you still must have fuel to propel the craft, and that [fuel] is human emotion.*

157

Opportunity: It now looks as if we have a process to change ourselves, and our realities. But as we all already know, it's not that easy. What's missing? If we change our thoughts, we can change our realities. Well, there's more.

The best example I can go back to is the computer, our own little PC's. We have a hard drive with a working program in place. It has been patched, up-graded and possibly even gotten a few viruses. But it is what we have been running all our lives. It helps us to make decisions and provides information for all sorts of situations. We know it and trust it. Why should we change it? Occasionally, we may become aware of a weak section where we ask for outside assistance, but, on average, it suits us.

Now here, someone comes along with a new "magical" upgrade. With it you can "supposedly" solve all those sticky problems you have been working around for years. Well, you might, just not go for it. Your interior skeptic says, "It sounds too good to be true, so it probably isn't true."

If you do get the program and bring it home, that doesn't mean it's on your PC. First, it must be installed. You may chicken out here. It could wipe out your hard drive all together if you make a mistake. But, let's say you have the will and courage to put this new upgrade into effect in your life. You put in the new disc and begin the process. Now you must power up the PC and see if things are different. But wait! How do you "power up" your life, your thoughts, and your ideas? This then becomes the next big problem. I was cautioned here by Mr. "B." Thought alone does not create, but thought powered or propelled by emotions creates.

R: "I have recently read an article, *Beyond Reality*, by Mark Buchanan" *(Ref. 19)*. **B: "Yes."** R: "Does this article do what I think it does and explain how our thoughts interact with and change matter?" **B: "Yes, indeed it does."**

R: "Does it explain the process we know as energy bonding in the Voice Dialogue Process?" *B: "To a degree, yes."* R: "Actually then, what we think of as thought is the same as what he calls information energy." *B: "Yes, but remember, thoughts are dormant energies until emotions propel them. Emotions give form to thought."*

Maybe then can we reuse the words, courage and will, or possibly, trust and faith, as the emotional engines to power up our new thoughts and ideas, so we can become a new creation. I think the answer is, yes, but then we must ask more questions about our emotions. What are they? Where do they come from? At this point, I must have subconsciously asked for clarification on the concept of emotion because he called me in and gave me the following information.

B: "R-o-g-e-r, This is in response to your desire for clarity about emotions, dominion, and relationship."

"Emotions are instinctual innately within all of humanity, and emotions are as varied as there are numbers of individuals upon your planet. An emotional experience is a very personalized process, for what you believe, understand, think, speak, and act upon, is as personal as, and as complex as all the components that make you who you are. A single set of circumstances can create and affect individuals very differently because of their past experiences and the complexities, that is their composite, are varied and different. It does not mean that one is right, or one is wrong. It simply means, it is based upon who they are and their composites."

"Triggering mechanisms for emotions are equally as varied. If a single set of circumstances triggers a set of emotions in you, and a different set in the Andrew and a different set in

the Kitty and the Jack, it is simply because of the differences in your composites. Emotions are propellants for creativity of thoughts and ideas and, of course, eventually actions. If you find that emotions are creating difficulty, or a particular set of emotions are creating difficulty, you would have need to explore within yourself what those triggering mechanisms are and begin to re-define them for yourself."

"And understanding, once again, you are only responsible for your emotions. You have no control, nor responsibility for how another individual or a group of individuals responds or reacts to their own emotions. You did not create their emotions, and you do not have any control of them. Do you understand this, I speak?" R: "Yes."

R: "It's my understanding that emotion interacts with thought to create form. And perception within our thoughts creates emotion. Is that right?"

B: "Emotion is the propellant that gives form to any number of creative processes. Perception about which has been created—How can I explain this? If you look at a color and Sam looks at a color, and this one looks at a color, and someone else does, you are going to see what you already perceive that color is. You may see it as Azure Blue. This one may see it as Turquoise Blue. Sam may see it as Sky Blue, and some one else may see it as a different color. Now if that one object or that one color is prevalent, how can others see it differently? Perception: Where does perception originate? Learning, past experiences, past memories of other life times, all of these things are a cognitive process that creates perception as you grow and mature. Do you understand?"

R: "I think so, but it seems like there is a circular pattern here. Perception creates emotion and that emotion creates perception." *B: "Not necessarily, because you can have perception without an emotion, and you certainly can have an emotion that's simply a gut emotion without any perception. Do you understand?"* R: "I think I'm missing something. The intent, now, how does the intent figure into this?" *B: "Let's see if we can explain."* R: "To secure change about my emotions, I have to look at the intent." *B: "That's correct."*

R: "And then, adjust the intent." *B: "Yes. If it's your desire to, let's say, change anger into a more productive emotion, maybe compassion. In order to do this, you have to understand and know what the anger served, because you see, nothing occurs without serving some purpose. Now it may not be a positive purpose, but it is a purpose."*

"So, if your anger served to allow you to communicate (because you had to wait until the anger was so explosive, then you could say all those things that had been suppressed) then; anger served as a communication tool. Or if your anger was born out of say, sibling rivalry—And were not saying any of this is accurate. We are just giving examples—and you were being bullied as a child and you suppressed all of that until you became so angry that you struck back. Then your anger was a tool of survival or being seen or heard. So first, you need to identify what purpose the anger served, and you can transfer intent to desire. It is not your desire to have anger or all of these other emotions that are detrimental to the human body, and you desire to have more positive things. But first, the goal is to identify what need that emotion served, and then you can fulfill your desire because you can identify what it was that it served and then change it to the more positive. Do you understand?" R: "Yes, I think I finally got it." *B: "Good."*

R: "What is the energy emotion? How does it work? Does it all come out of Gods love?" ***B: "That's where it originates, but by the time it goes through an individual's composite of experiences, it can be come distorted, convoluted, umm, perceptually erroneously interpreted."***

So, now we have it. The reason change is so difficult to "power up," so to speak, is because our emotional energy may be distorted, convoluted and erroneously interpreted. Because individual sets of past circumstances may be erroneously interpreted, they may trigger fear or anger instead of trust and love. The new idea is then "deleted" by the fear energy, and we continue down the old familiar path of disease and problems. As Mr. B says, to stop the emotional pattern that is causing us difficulty, we must look at the mechanisms that trigger these emotions and redefine them. I think it was "Pogo" that once said something like this, *"We have found the enemy and they are us."*

To be effective then, and to make use of the opportunity to look at our thoughts and change, we must also be willing to look at our feelings and emotions because one can't happen without the other. By looking at our emotions and understanding the thoughts and energies within us that triggers them, we can redefine these emotions, therein freeing up the love and trust necessary for change.

Just as a review here, we must state a few basics of emotional theory: We create all of our emotions. We do this by the thoughts we hold about sets of circumstances we have experienced.

Some error thoughts we may hold are: Another person made me angry. Wrong! We make ourselves angry because it feels better to be angry than to accept the responsibility for our actions.

This person makes me feel really good. Wrong! You have chosen to feel good and given the power away to another in your mind. Perhaps you do not love yourself enough to think you can make yourself happy.

A robber frightened me with his gun. Wrong! You have learned to be frightened when your life is in danger. Perhaps a parent used fear to manipulate you or to be more cautious when you were young.

This could go on and on. There are books written about it. We attribute many of our feelings to others. This is all incorrect. These ideas must change, or you will not be able to take charge of your emotions and change your life.

When you understand how to identify the source of your emotions and feelings, you can start the long hard process of changing those that are now originating in your subconscious. As you do this, your subconscious becomes more part of your conscious mind and awareness.

This one statement may help you own these emotions. "We create or co-create with others everything that happens in our lives." Some may think this is a ridiculous statement, but if we believe spirit, it is correct. The real problem is some of our lives are created from our subconscious minds, without our awareness, and some are created from humanity's group conscious mind of which we are a part. In situations created by the group consciousness, we are only responsible for how we react to it.

If we can really believe this idea, we can then get some insight as to the thoughts we hold in our subconscious mind. We do this by looking at what is going on all around us in our everyday lives. If we find our VCR missing, maybe our subconscious thought is we were watching movies too much. Or, if our boss is continuously victimizing us, maybe we don't

163

believe at the subconscious level that we deserve a good employer.

I will drop this subject here, not because it's not important, but because I believe we have made the point. This message is the key in this entire study. The understanding of our own software package, our thoughts and emotions connected to them, is the real key to surviving the upcoming Earth changes. We then will be able to create a new being in this great opportunity window. That being will be able to create a livable reality using its thoughts and emotions. According to some, that reality will be instantaneously a fact. The key to learning how to do this, is to fully own the reality you are now creating.

Barbara Brennen: As I was trying to work out the effects of magnetism on the human body, I also became acquainted with Barbara Brennen's book, *Hands of Light.* As I read it I became aware that I must understand much beyond the magnetic effects on the human body. This book is a great scientific work. The only problem is that science is so far behind, that it doesn't seem to realize the theoretical impact of this work.

The first thing that I was able to see is Barbara's work can be used as an example. The energy fields I had been trying to describe on the solar level were exactly what she had been describing on the human level. The implication being, that in a holographic world, I may be able to use the descriptions of the human aura to describe the much greater, but similar fields of our solar system.

This can see in the outline below. (15) p - 139

Human		Solar System

First level   .... Physical .... Physical
Second level ... Ethic (electromagnetic) .... Magnetic
Third level ...... Emotional (photon Base) .... Light photon base
Fourth level .... Mental Ideas (Morphogenetic) ..God's thoughts
Fifth level +.... Astral - Spiritual - Creator .... God's love

As you can see, the human model does appear to apply, at least, in the first three levels. I'm sure most agree that the potential for the mental and spiritual human bodies to guide us in the manifestation of our creation also exists. If this is the case it, at least, poses the question. Are these two levels also going to be found in the solar system as would be expected in a true hologram?

This provides a whole new area of development for the study of the material. Up until now we have simply called it space soup. If the simple photon that can readily be entrained is the essence of the magnetic aspect of space soup, then the teachable or variable photon discovered by Mark Buchanan, may be the message carrier of the space soup environment. We may think of this little variable photon as the carrier of thought that has already been energized by emotion. Mr. Buchanan has already demonstrated this in the laboratory.

Like human DNA, energized by emotion, can entrain light photons (as explained by Greg Braden). Some sort of creative thought, energized by the Creator's emotion, could be entraining the flow of photons between the Sun and Jupiter.

These photons, entrained by the universal consciousness as indicated by Mr. "B," may well affect the sunlight differently than normal unorganized space soup photons. I know this may seem strange when viewed in Newtonian physics thinking, but

165

if we stretch our minds and try to look at some of the new theories that state all things are part of a whole, it then gives a concept that we can use to bind the whole together.

Now I want to introduce you to some teachings of Mr. "B" from several years ago. We will be able to see how one primary thought, held deeply by many, can cause a circular pattern and prevent growth.

Upon The Spiral Stairs

I think most can now accept that we are in part electromagnetic beings, at least, in the third dimension. I believe most would also agree that we are more than that. Religions for eons have spoken of the human soul, that part of humanity that is eternal and goes beyond the physical. The following discussion will address this aspect of us that we think of as the soul. It is a part of who and what we are. It is also the root of one of mankind's greatest misconceptions. I will quote some of Mr. B's teaching on duality as part of this discussion.

Duality Consciousness, Mr. "B"

B: *"It originated when mankind on this plane of existence lost its ability to focus upon the God-center within. Because they had conscious intellectual process and knew there was a Creator Being—the Creator Father, or by what ever name It is called—and they had lost the ability to identify it as being within themselves; they placed it in some obscure external region."*

"Then they began to build palaces, kingdoms, and mansions within this obscure region. Of course, they had to place inhabitants within this newly built city, so they placed angels and cherubim, and the Creator Father upon an enormous throne, created of the purest of material possessions on this

plane. Then they placed mythological beings, religious teachers, prophets and all matters of deity. They built Earthly edifices of their obscure city, and man has been in search of a way to reach his own obscurity. What needs to be released for the greatest understanding, and for the immortal peace that all are inherently aware of is this obscurity."

"For my dearly beloved children, it is all within your hands, your heart, your soul. Your very being is that which you call the heavenly realm. That kingdom that has been built and placed in an external environment is, in truth, within. That magnificent Creator Father and all of his children and descendants are within the souls and faces of each upon this planet."

"You need to place that kingdom in its proper environment, within. You need to take a few moments each day and meditate in your cathedral, your heavenly realm. For it is more beautiful than what your most descriptive words have endeavored to portray."

In these words Mr. "B" tells us we are god, like Christ, our example said. He is the Son of God, and we are made in His image. God is not in a remote place called heaven that we must struggle to get to. If we can accept that God is a part of us and a part of all beings and all things in this third dimension, then we can better see how we can co-create our own reality with God. Why is it so hard to say, "I am god?" I think the answer is quite understandable. Let's get more from Mr. "B" directly on this.

B: "For those who are standing upon the threshold of true awareness, there is that resonation, that remaining relic of fear, that you dare not recognize yourself to be the god you are. For those who step through that doorway of awareness, the beauty and immortal peace is ever present."

"After you have become comfortable with entering your cathedral and become familiar with that immortal peace, you are fully prepared to master all things. The difficulty with mastery is not in learning the skill, but in identification of the obstacles that stand as barriers between you and your mastership. These barriers are present in the majority of humanity in variable degrees. They are: ego, fear, lack of worthiness, degrees of social consciousness, and erroneous concepts placed upon you like yokes by religious and educational institutions."

"Most of humanity's religious teachings are filled with "cannots," placed there by persons who wish to have control over your thought process and physical activities. It is one of the greater obstacles for mankind to overcome. If you but take your own religious writings and remove all of the negative connotations and concepts, what one would have is a master plan or blueprint for the evolvement of spiritual attainment."

I want to talk of the phrase, *"remaining relic of fear."* I believe, for me, this is the key problem. Suppose I was to go into a Christian church and state, "Jesus Christ didn't physically die for my sins. He lived and died to teach us. Like him, we are God also." I would find this very difficult to do. It may be, because at some time, I have been persecuted for such a statement. It may be because Jesus Christ gave his life when he claimed to be God. But regardless, it would be very hard to do.

Well, we must not limit the "Christ" by putting him off somewhere. We must learn to recognize the "Christ" in others, all things and ourselves. This will allow us to become creators of our own reality, consciously. Mr. "B" points out how this affects our concept of death.

B: *"When mankind began to separate himself in consciousness from that which created him, he lost the ability to recognize and act upon his own immorality. ... He began the process of building cellular memories of death and began to promote the illusion that death would allow one to inhabit a holy place where the Creator Father dwelt. Mankind began to create the illusion that death was a part of the divine plan to reunite the Creator with the creation."*

"This is indeed error of thought and illusion. For death is not a natural process of humanity but a created process of humanity. As my Brother (Jesus Christ) *and others taught, you can overcome this process, and you can create an immortal being."*

"Death is not always a fatality. It is, but a thought created in the minds of men. When you truly identify the holy self and all that it is intended to be, then you have transcended that which you have called death. For the holy being is not altered by the process of physical death. It merely allows one to re-inhabit another physical body and the continuation of experiences and expression upon this plane of existence that was chosen by the soul. Once you master that illusion, the process becomes unnecessary, for you can transcend to other planes without the process of death. It has been done for thousands and thousands upon thousands of years. In all religious writings, it is so stated that there was and shall be those who ascend to the higher planes of expression without the process of death."

I cannot here present the entire teaching of Mr. "B" in the little paper *Upon The Spiral Stairs*, but I believe I have given you enough to start you consciously upon the spiral stairs within your own being. We do not need to wait in fear for the Earth mother to go through her cycles of change. We are part of her, and so we must go through our own cycles of change. We are told that many came to Earth at this time to be part of this great challenge. You may be one, if you can remember who and what you are. It is no time to be timid, no time to believe you are a victim. We will be what we believe we are. In this time of change, I hope you can believe you are the God of your own creation.

If we can remember the energy of creation is the "E"-motion of God's love, and if we can put away our fear and recreate our emotional composite to also radiate accurately God's love, we will cease to be part of the problem and instead become part of the solution.

Mr. "B" discussion

R: "It appears the question of religion goes back to Moc-Qua-To-Noc and BaSeth (two of my past lives) also. Have I always understood about the spirit of the Christ in all living things? Could you explain some?"

B: *"Certainly, and yes. The energy that is perceived as being that of the Christ is present in all things. It is the energy that is renewal. It is the energy that is rebirth. It is the energy that is hopeful. It is the energy that is healing. It is the energy that is love greater than self, the ego self. It is manifest in all things. It is manifest in the birth of an offspring. It is manifest in the death of an elder. It is renewal. It is the cycle of life itself. That is the Christ energy. It is the energy that has all potential, and it is the energy that when the ego is separated, reaches out to join in common bond with another of its own kind, whether it is an animal of the forest, or the fish of the sea or humanity. It is the same energy. Do you understand?"* R: "Yes."

How to become one with the Christ within

I asked Mr. "B" for information on this. Here are some of his answers. This first question was about healing myself.

R: "What primary foods should I focus on if I want my body to be better able to handle this frequency and electrolytes?" *B: "A lot of grains and green vegetables, and a good level of protein."* R: "So I can eat steak, and it won't hurt me as long as I stay away from the fat?" *B: " Well, protein can be gained from other than beef, but you can eat steak infrequently, and it will not harm you."*

R" "Learning to harmonize our resonant pulse. I'm assuming this can be done with the emotion of love. Is that correct?" *B: "Yes."* R: "We can't harmonize out of fear because that sticks us." *B: "Well, no, it takes you in a Vortex"*

R: "If we harmonize with someone who is at a lower vibration or frequency, will it lower our vibration or frequency?" *B: "Indeed it shall."*

R: "When we harmonize with God?" *B: "It raises our frequency, but when you begin to try to balance your energy or harmonize with anything that's of a lower frequency, whatever is, at that lower frequency is going to take from you and add to itself."* R: "OK." *B: "And if you aren't aware and cognitive, you will become drained. But then it's not but just a short journey until you do not exist in a physical form."*

R: "When people harmonize with God, do they see this white light?" ***B: "Yes."*** R: "When I see the purple light in my third eye, does this mean I'm harmonizing with God?" ***B: "Yes, that is with the consciousness of the Creator. You are doing what is called a mind link of a sort."*** R: "That is what I am supposed to be doing?" ***B: " Oh, Indeed."*** R: "OK."

R: "There was a part of that where it seemed to me if we were able to take the Christ Child within us . . ." **B: *"Yes."*** R: . . . "where there is like a perfect pattern. If we can take that and replay it (as a piece of software) in our bodies and correct the errors in our thought processes . . ."

B: "Oh, absolutely. That is true for all people. That is the message of the Christ Child. The internal perfection being made manifest in a physical form to overcome all challenges."

R: "Is the best way to do that to meditate on that, or just imagine it happening in my body?" **B: *"Yes, and seeing that perfection, believing that perfection and acting upon that perfection."***

On 8/3/98 I talked to Mr. "B" about his teachings in the paper, *Upon The Spiral Stairs*. The questions and answers are below.

R: "Did you give XXXXXX a message for me that I could find the humanity parts of my book in the writings, *Upon The Spiral Stairs*?" **B: *"No."***

R: "I did study *The Spiral Stairs*." **B: *"There is good information contained therein, but I would have given you a message for you."***

R: "I would like to talk about this some, this duality of con-sciousness." *B: "Yes."* R: "It seams to me that this is kind of like the primary problem with humanity." *B: "Certainly."*

R: "As long as we hold this separation, there is no way to know who we are or what we are. Is that true?" *B: "That's correct. You may have glimpse, and you may have intellectual knowledge, but you will not be confident, and you will not be the manifestation of all that you are."*

R: "The teachings on page 4 and 5, especially that part, "the remaining relic of fear, that you dare not recognize yourself as the god you are . . . Is this caused by the persecution?"

B: "It is caused by a great number of things, but it is ulti-mately caused by the histories of all of humanity, not just a single individual. When man separated from God in con-sciousness because God never separated from man, it began this series of errors that further separated man in conscious-ness from the innate God aura. Do you understand?"

R: "Well, I think I do. As I was studying this, it became clear to me that as long as we look outside, we cannot solve what's inside. And I just didn't know how we got there. But I don't know that it matters." *B: "It only matters in as much as you understand in all levels of your being that God never, ever, left mankind."*

R: "It is appropriate for me to use some of these words in this book?" *B: "Certainly."* R: "I felt a little bit ill at ease because I can't use as much as the public should be aware of. I don't know if I can excerpt the right parts." *B: "We will assist you."*

R: "The second part of what seemed to be man's primary problem they must deal with, is this the concept of original sin?" ***B: "Yes."*** R: "Is that true?" ***B: "Well, understanding that the word sin is merely just an error, and it goes back to man's original concept or when man begin to look elsewhere for God. If you can understand it in that context, it is . . . umm, a primary teaching. Do you understand?"***

R: "Yes, I was thinking it was error, but if you think of it as our separation, then we did create original (error) sin." ***B: "Yes."***

R: "The same would be true of Heaven and Hell. With the separation, we created them." ***B: "Yes."***

I want to point out the next section was very special. Whenever I listened to the tape of the following questions, I am deeply moved. Mr. "B" tells the Story of Jesus on the cross in a way one would talk of a brother he loved very much. As he personalized the story for my friends and I in Gettysburg, it made the story real in a way it never has been before.

The Resurrection Story

R: "It appears the church in this period (implied at the time of Christ) went to extremes to declare that Jesus was God, but also that he was very different from us. Did this kind of make this separation?" ***B: "Well, by this time the separation was well entrenched. And Jesus was God. Just as you are and everyone else is. God sent an emissary*** (an agent to advance the interests of another)***, if you would like to use that word, to teach that nothing in the human condition is impossible, including death. See, death is not a finality. It was never proclaimed to be a finality, but humanity entrenched themselves in this thought. They entrenched themselves in the thought if you had an illness you were going to succumb to that illness.***

They were entrenched in the thoughts that hatred, war and conflict were justified. Jesus taught none of these things are justified. Love, compassion, kindness, and forgiveness are the way to overcome all adversarial conflicts, internal and external, and that by merely damaging or wounding a body does not ensure that person's removal. You can inflict mortal wounds upon a body, but it's not going to rid you of whatever perpetrated that wound you inflicted. And he proved it.

And even when they put him on this very macabre fixture called a cross, he would not succumb to their will and damn them. Instead, he forgave them. And it was that power, that love, that unconditional love that when they wrapped him in a cloth and put him in a tomb, that was nothing more than a rock. A solid rock of granite that had been hollowed out. And they laid him there, and they put a huge boulder, like the ones you see on your battlefield here, in front, and they placed guards. They could not stop by mortal methods that power of love. You have heard the saying, "The burning embers of love." Well, it truly occurred in that tomb. For when that power of love regenerated that body, it seared the cloth in which he was wrapped, and he walked out, literally, figuratively, and in actuality. He walked out of a sealed tomb.

That's an amazing story, yet it is true. And he tells those who see him "Do not touch me." Do you understand why?"

R: "No." *B: "You should because you are writing a book about it."* R: "Is it the magnetics?"

B: *"Absolutely. If anyone would have touched him at that point they would have been almost electrocuted. He had to keep them at bay until he could contain that electrical energy within his body. Because, later they did touch him and that's documented in your biblical readings. The man Thomas, because he didn't believe, the man Jesus said, "Place your hand," and he did."*

I loved the way Mr. "B" told this story, but I still struggled with the concept that we are responsible and create our realities here in this world. This brought up many theories like the one below.

R: "Is this statement true? Personal separation from the God within us makes us willing victims to the pretend gods of others." *B: "Certainly."*

R: "I was trying to perceive how the people of the holocaust could be held responsible for the creation of that reality, and that's the only thing I could come up with. Is that accurate?" *B: "It is accurate. It's not the only reason, but it's accurate."*

R: "I have been starting to work with the concept of God and cathedral within me." *B: "Yes."* R: "Do you perceive I am on the right track here?" *B: "Oh, indeed, yes."*

Now let's get back to our model created by Barbara Brennen for a moment. If we believe in the duality as outlined by Mr. "B," We have an error thought created in the mind body. This error thought says for all practical purposes, the spirit body does not exist. It is the sole realm of God and cannot be reached until death.

While in reality, it (our sacred cathedral) is only in this spirit body we each have, that is where the perfect pattern of the Christ is held. That is why it is so important to learn to know and love who you are in total.

Barbara Brennen has created in her world a place for the spirit body of the Christ to exist. It exists in her and her patients within the aura, which extends the furthest out. By changing ideas held in the mental body, what Mr. "B" called the "individuals composite of experience," she is able to bridge from the emotional body to the perfect pattern of the Christ in the spirit body. This process heals all the way back down to the physical body energy level. This is the primary secret of her success.

10 Integration of a Holistic Universe

In my opinion Barbara Brennen has moved beyond the dualism of the majority of the humankind. She has done this by accepting that she is one with God at her spiritual level. She has been able to contact the complete whole pattern of the Christ within herself. Her mental ability has allowed her to create an accurate mind-body from this spiritual pattern. By doing these two things, she is able to interpret her historical experiences in the glowing aura of God's love, this aura of love that permeates and heals the etheric body. Of course the physical body is also healed because it forms on the Morphogenetic pattern in the etheric body. She has not only done this for herself, but she is able to teach this to others.

Gregg Braden is also bridging the gap, and bringing the human experience and the universal experience together in a holistic manor. These two teachers are starting to anchor these ideas, as Braden would say, in the single universal reality of human kind.

Mr. "B" tells us how these ideas are formed and energized with human thought and emotion. They are then cast out into the void where time and space do not exist. In this void they gather together with energy from similar idea energy packets. As these packets of energy gain strength, they start to take form in matter. They may become a book, a class taught, a trip taken, or an experience shared. This creates more similar energy packets until a threshold amount is achieved. Then, as in *The Hundredth Monkey* Story, everyone becomes aware. This awareness is reflected in a higher frequency, and the higher frequency creates a whole new material world.

I believe that is what we are about. I think the universal field is now changing phase, and we are a part of that change. We are not separate from the universe any more than we are separate from God. We will change or be reformed in this process. It appears that these concepts that we as yet do not understand in quantum physics are the laws that will govern these changes.

One person who has described her personal experiences in working with and experiencing the creative energies in nature is Machaelle Small Wright. In her book titled, *Behaving as if the God in All Things Mattered*, she describes the process of co-creating actual physical matter in her garden. She does this with the aid of spiritual energies which many people refuse to believe exist.

"As soon as I connected, I felt myself lift (vibrationally) to a very familiar level—the level where astral traveling is done. There we waited until, suddenly, I felt a third energy enter my awareness. We had been joined by the energy of the manure. With great care, we all three moved "down" in vibration more slowly than I had ever experienced in meditation—or perhaps it was simply more clear than I had ever experienced. As we moved from one level to the next, I could feel the shift in the manure energy. Eventually, I felt the manure take on a sense of physicalness—I sensed atoms, then molecules, then cells. I sensed from within the nature energy—and eventually, even a slight smell. When I felt it had completed the process, I opened my eyes, and there before me was the cubic foot of manure."

"I'm not going to say that I took this casually. For sometime, I just stared at the manure, thinking about what had happened." (16) p - 41.

This story tells me we already have people within our midst that have the very same skills the ancients used to move the giant stones. People, who like Machaelle, have managed to unlearn the logic that keeps most of us trapped in our limited vision. This book is a must read for those of you who wish to understand the principals I am discussing here.

Perhaps nothing supports Machaelle's work more than the ancient Zapotec creation legend, found in *Lord of the Dawn*.

> *"This was not enough, not enough of him, he lit the sky with lightning and sent forth his greatest sacrifices, this came in the form of Guardians of the Earth. Tiny spirits, Pockwatchie spirits, spirits of the mountains, guardians of her breast, spirits of the rocks, guardians of her love, spirits of the rivers, guardians of her blood, spirits of the valleys, guardians of her growth, spirits for all things of the Earth, and no particle of dust nor grain of sand was left without part of his spirit. And the "little people" danced through the darkness on the Earth, singing the love song the clouds had taught them."* (18) p- 38,39.

This describes the same world Machaelle has relocated, a world alive with the spirit of God, a world we must all consider, if we believe Mr. "B" when he says, **"God never, ever left man."** This ancient story represents laws that are new to us in one sense, yet as old as the ancients in another deeper sense. The concept of one great creator is not new. The concept of the soul and the soul's energy is not new. The ability to see auras and to feel energies is not new. These ideas have always been held by a few prophets and teachers, people like Jesus who loved unconditionally in the face of unspeakable fear and anger all around him.

We are not breaking new ground here. We are just trying to clear away the error thoughts our limited understanding of science has created. These error thoughts have helped us create the fears that blind and separate us from each other and the God within us.

I hope in this book I can do this. We still have time to learn. The reality is the Earth changes are just a more intense arena in which these lessons can be learned. As we learn through new scientific tools how to read and interpret the world around us, we will also remember old tools we once used—like dowsing. I believe almost any one with a simple crystal on a string can locate the emotional energy swirling around our body in our chakras. Sensitive fingers can feel energy loss through a damaged place in the etheric body. The more of this we are exposed to, the more our awareness will change. We will be able to open to the reality of the levels of energies that creates a total us.

We may relearn to feel Earth's energy as the Indians of New England did when they located their stone chambers. We may again stand on the top of a rock mountain to be recharged by the Universal Energy Field as James Redfield explains in his book, *The Celestine Prophecy*. We will look forward with excitement to the time of changes. But first we must honor those who already have the skill. We must listen to those such as Machaelle Small Wright, Gregg Braden and Barbara Ann Brennan, for they are the pioneers. We must honor the native peoples who still remember.

I have been told the effect of the Earth changes have already started. Changes in the weather and effects on our emotions are already taking place. As we become more aware, we will be able to see these new realities unfold. There is no reason for fear and panic. These low frequency emotions will disappear in the reality of the higher frequency of unconditional love. As we develop a new more expanded vocabulary to describe these new experiences, humanity will fundamentally change.

When enough has made the change, it will be possible for all to make the change. At some sort of magical threshold, everyone will be able to see. At this time our whole world will become different. Imagine how the world would be if every one could see auras and heal as Barbara Brennen can. Mr. "B" assures us this is possible. It has not happened yet for mankind but it is possible. That is the primary message of the Christ. It is in the understanding of his word that he becomes our savior. We each have the sacred pattern of Christ within us. Through this we can become aware again that we are one with God, the very oneness we have so long sought after.

Mr. "B" Discussion:

R: "I believe you once said sound waves could be used to induce an altered state of consciousness. Is this safer than using magnetic variations?" *B: "It's not any safer, just different."* R: "What frequencies would be the best for that?" *B: "It would depend on the level of altered state of consciousness that one was endeavoring to achieve, but in the Baroque, are you familiar with this?"* R: "I'm not sure. The only thing I've heard is the 8 cycles or something like the Earth frequency." *B: "Yes, exactly."* R: "That's the frequency?" *B: "Yes."*

R: "It seems you could create a sound or frequency that would put people in an altered state. Is that true?" *B: "It would put some there."* R: "I was just curious if this could be done safely as an anesthesia or some thing." *B: "It could be, but it probably wouldn't be very well received, particularly in this country in which you dwell."*

R: "During the extreme yin state of 5/5/2000, what *of notice* will happen?" *B: "A great many things. It will be -- What is your term for this (waving arms)?"* R: "Fluctuating." *B: "Yes."* R: "Fluctuating emotional situations?" *B: "Emotional, in all circumstances, emotional, economics, climate, all."* R: "Is there anything that I and my family should do to prepare?" *B: "If you are aware, you are prepared because the chaos will not frighten you. You will understand it."* R: "Okay."

R: "You said that ancient man could be tracked by skeletal mitochondria. Is this currently being done or is it new science?" *B: "It is currently being done but very secretively."* R: "If I was to come out with this in this book it might create a new science for some?" *B: "Indeed."*

R: "Does a mountaintop focus yin or yang energy?" *B: "A mountaintop?"* R: "If you got on the peek of the mountain?" *B: "Not in great proportion, no."* R: "Does it have any kind of focus of the magnetic energy?" *B: "Oh, Yes."* R: "Then in the pyramid it was the magnetic energy they were working with." *B: "Indeed."* R: "Is it true the magnetic field in the sarcophagus of the Great Pyramid is non-existent or nearly non- existent?" *B: "Nearly non-existent is correct."*

R: "If we created the magnetic field with two large magnets as we talked about and put a small animal in, it would become catatonic or maybe even kill it?" *B: "It could very easily."* R: "Would that animal deteriorate or would it rather stay that way?" *B: "It would rather stay that way."* R: "Also, because no bacteria would be there?" *B: "That's correct."* (Check later to see if a photon vacuum could be used to preserve food).

R: "Was the cause of this excessive heat this summer (summer of 1999) the Venus Effect?" *B: "Yes."*

R: "This galactic wave—The increase in heat is caused by the excess in photons? If this is true, doesn't it mean it will stay warmer?" *B: "It will never get as cool as it once was, yes."*

R: "In my study of DNA and the I—Ching, I have been reading the book, *Rhythms and Visions*. There is a drawing of DNA. Is that accurate?" *B: "Fairly accurate, yes."* R: "It shows a square in the middle, then it goes to a hexagon, then to a pentagon?" *B: "Yes."* R: "Do these DNA forms relate directly to the Earth energy and the Jupiter/Saturn energy and the Venus energy?" *B: "Yes, it does."* R: "That developed because of a harmonious vibration?" *B: "And the energy— How will I explain this?—It is a harmonic energy, but it is also the same pattern as the distance between the strands of DNA would equate or represent the distance in between these planets, particularly when they are in certain alignments. Do you understand?"* R: "I think I probably will if I study it more. It's like a holograph." *B: "Absolutely."*

R: "When organic matter burns it gives off heat and light. Does this mean organic forms capture photons?" *B: "Yes, of course."* R: "So the photons are inside these little structures in the human DNA, I suppose." *B: "Yes, that is correct."*

R: "I've come to this conclusion a few times. I'm not sure if it is accurate but, umm . . . in the pentagon that's created by Venus with its relationship with Earth, there is always a small error. Is this real or is it caused by our perception of space and time?"

B: "It is caused by your perception or human perception and also . . . Humanity, no matter how brilliant they perceive they are, do not have very true, accurate mathematics equations as it relates to this particular subject we are speaking of."

R: "So the same would be true of the conjunction triangle of Jupiter and Saturn?" *B: "Certainly."* R: "So these errors are just errors?" *B: "It is human error."*

11 How to Ride the Orb

Chambers of Time

Mr. "B" did drop a bombshell on me when he said the magnetic null zone was a *no-time* zone. "*No-time*," how did it relate to a magnetic field? In the previous chapters we looked at who we are and how we fit in. In this last chapter we will try to bring it all together. Mankind's physical and spiritual riding on an Earth moving on what seems to be its own process, but in reality, is all one big plan.

Now I believe the key to understanding isn't the magnetic field, it's us. Mr. "B" had already told me we are electromagnetic beings, or at least the part of us in the third dimension is. In fact, the whole third dimension is probably an electromagnetic fabrication. Aren't the basic elements held together by the electron charges on them? Then don't they combine to make molecules that recombine to make organisms and go on to what are call higher life forms, of which we are one? Sure, that's it. We are just huge electromagnetic structures organized around a thought (software idea), that our soul creates for us as our third-dimensional reality.

It's all so simple. That's why thoughts create. Everything else here is already an electromagnetic creation. Only the thoughts and emotions change. A thought once held and energized by emotion only has one creation. That's how prediction takes place. If we can't change our thoughts or our emotions, we continue to move through our software program from birth to death to a predictable end. When we recognize that we create our realities with our thoughts through our exercise of free will, then they no longer bind us.

But now we must get back to N*o-time* and magnetism. The third or physical dimension is only possible in the world of the electromagnetic field. Remove the charged field. *Voila*! The third dimension will change. Physical matter exists, but not as we know it. So thought is an energy and at the same time it is a form of energy shaper when it is energized by emotion. Again, the best model I can use is that our thoughts make up our software package.

Quantum Physics

The answer to how thought works in this electronic body of ours can be found in quantum physics. The universal space soup is made up of photons. Some are regular and others are informational, a name given by researcher Mark Bucahanan. These photons that the researcher called informational cannot be tested. When asked the question if they are positive or negative, they indicate they are either positive or negative. This concept goes far beyond the scope of this book, but it is important if the reader can perceive this one point. In quantum theory physics, there is a particle that can and probably does carry our thought patterns. It is temporary in its action, but it can induce its pattern on regular photons that it comes in contact with. In this way, our thoughts function as a sort of software update package. Only they shape real matter and energy. Many argue, "How can our thoughts create our reality?" Well here in this little informational photon is the process.

There is another part to this little photon. It is connected in a circular fashion when cupped with a matched pair. This allows it to provide information both forward and backward in time. So now we not only have a way for thoughts to create, but they can create both forward and backward in time. Mr. "B" has implied that in a somewhat lower electromagnetic field, this ability may be enhanced. He said that the stone chambers and Kivas that were laid out on magnetic anomalies could function as time traveling devices. Why is it important for us to understand and believe this? The answer is quite simple. If we are going to be effective in dealing with the upcoming N*o-time*, we need a process under which to act. Awareness of the possible future may enable some to make adjustments to assure a better chance of humanity's survival.

Awareness of our thought energies, conscious and subconscious, becomes essential to changing our physical realities. If we are unaware of a subconscious thought, it will continue to create in our third dimensional body and world. This is why we must understand the nature of the multiple realities in the universe and why we must not blame, but totally own everything in our physical reality as part of our creation. If we don't own something or how we react to something, then our actions are coming from our subconscious. This must be true because it has nowhere else to originate.

The old cliché, "We cannot have our cake and eat it too." applies here. In other words, if we do control our reality, we must control all of our reality either as individuals or groups. These realities will be created if we know it or not. We do not create the original energies themselves. The universe provides that. The universe also provides the rules or truths about how it all works. Our task, if we choose to accept it, is to create a software package of thoughts and ideas to operate within this dimension. Also, we must create an emotional context under which to energize it.

When we chose to incarnate, we have at the soul level decided to do this in concert with many others. Our thought energy, or Soul energy, is only strong enough to create our own reality. Of course, we are a part of the "whole" which creates the rest of reality. If we "think" we are controlled by what's around us, we are, simply by default. This connects us to other energies we all come in contact with. These other energies do exist. They just do not have any "real" control over our reality. If we allow ourselves to be triggered by them, it is because we are unaware of that part of us which this "supposed outside" energy represents. Awareness of all the energies is the key then to being aware of the God within us.

So, "Personal dominion" issues are extremely critical. If you cannot separate your "personal dominion" from the "personal dominion" of another, you perceive yourself as a victim or hero in the joint reality! The "victim," the frightened little boy or girl, or the "hero," concerned savior adult, are erroneous and a creation of your negative ego in error thought. How can anyone be a victim in the reality they create themselves? They have created that reality as a place to learn and to grow. When we look to John Wayne as our hero to ride in and fix the situation, we assure ourselves we will continue to perceive ourselves in need of being rescued, struggling in the situation for the next several lifetimes if necessary until we see the error thought.

It seems that when we know what we are, God Incarnate, and why we are here, to do a spiritual task on this third dimensional plane, then it is really a matter of integrating these truths into our subconscious thoughts and routing out all the error thoughts.

Well, how does this all relate to these Earth changes and humanity's journey on this orb? Obviously, this is a school or training ground where we can learn to correct our error thoughts by being able to experience the end results of those thoughts. As we create humanity's history and futures in this dimension, we become aware that either history or future is just a projection forward or backward based on the thoughts and energies we hold today. As these thoughts and energies evolve, our history and our future seem to change.

Now as we become aware that we are and always have been able to create our future, it is no longer necessary to have a past where all that exists is ignorance. Now that we are aware that our current thoughts and energies will "self-destruct" us and most of the life on this planet is not adjusted, it is time to re-evaluate our thoughts.

Yes, when Mr. "B" gave me the information that without a magnetic field the illusion we call the third dimension did not exist in time as we perceive it, I got the feeling that it was more like a still picture of our current thoughts, not coming from anywhere, not going anywhere: just a snapshot in time of a group of thoughts and energies: then, the real illusion, of what the third dimension is, came home.

This is all very esoteric, but what is there to be done with such information in the context of this book? After all, this is a book about third dimensional realities . . . or is it? We are aware now that there appear to be men/gods acting in our historic past. It appears that the playing field, our orb (Earth) may change. Is the concept, "It's graduation time," familiar? We accept that the universe in the third dimension is finite or, at least, it is fixed by its rules, the rules of the thought that created it. Therefore, we can postulate that its purpose may be more than a school for human souls to experience. It may be a school for much beyond what we can ever conceive. Why then should we not believe that our teachers or schoolmaster, the conceiver of Earth, may not want to see his classroom destroyed by one unwilling student, his little being he calls humanity?

This little being thinks it's divided into millions of separate students, when in reality he/she is just one. It is sort of like a mint plant gone wild in the corner of the garden, crowding out the carrots and beats. The gardener is required to remove some the mint each year if the garden is to survive.

How can the being called mint be taught his personal dominion if he feels he has the right to destroy the personal dominion of the rest of the garden. This is not new to the gardener. Other energies have tried to take over the garden. He/she must always correct these erroneous beliefs if the beings and the garden are to grow and evolve.

So, as a small sprig of mint in this garden called Earth, what am I to do? If I were to set down a history of mint, I might see where I/we made our mistakes. First, it is not "we" millions of little parts of humanity. It is "I" humanity. There are millions of others in the garden—the animals, the plants, insects, and elements—all of them with a creative thought or their own "software." These small pieces of the universe live much as we do.

The lead crystal born deep in the molten core of the "Orb" is cooked to a liquid state, and as it cools, it follows its software pattern to make the perfect little cubes we know as (bauxite) lead ore. Who are we to think our lessons are more important to the creator than these, and yet, we are no less important either. The farmer loves his plants, and he will do his best to grow those he sees as beautiful and pleasing to him. If he must trim a rose to get a flower, he will. The rose learns to know this, and we must learn to know this. Humanity must also learn its place in the garden.

Large numbers of us have been cast out of the garden before. The gardener is God acting through Gaia, the creative spirit of the Earth, of which we are part. In one sense we are the co-creator of these upcoming changes. Our Earth mother energy is well aware of how to accomplish the task she must do. The difficult student is given difficult lessons or tasks, and so it may be for us. To stay in the garden where the lessons are more pleasant, we must study hard and learn. The prophets seem to be telling us that graduation is coming soon. It is time to gather in the harvest from the garden, and to cast the weeds on the compost pile where they will become the source for some new experiment.

Why would we then create the situation we are currently approaching? This can only be understood in the terms of humanity, the "I", or the one. Our souls are part of the bigger soul of the whole humanity as well as part of God Itself. Our soul knows the energy, that we think of as the individual third-dimensional being, cannot be lost in the process we call death. It can only be lost to itself if it denies it is part of the One, the

Eternal Creator. Therefore a test that will bring it closer to the realization that it is part of God is welcome.

I believe the gardener will want to keep his little student, humanity. As with the sunflowers, some of the plants have produced seeds, there are some with loving flowers. If he brings a cold winter, those with loving flowers will create viable seeds. These seeds will survive the cold winter's test. In the springtime, they will again grow and blossom. Those who were unable to love and create seeds will not be continued in the next season. In the real world garden, not all plants will reproduce. But the gardener will protect and cherish the seeds of those that do. In this way, the little being (humanity) grows each new season, loving every individual part of itself, testing new thoughts, ideas and combinations such as black ones, red ones, white ones and yellow ones, and mixing them in the garden to produce the very best; therein, producing something worthy of decorating the gardener's dwelling.

The racial mind, the mind of the being we call humanity, holds many thoughts and ideas. Some "truths" and some "error thoughts." I "write" and "think" to improve the truths and reduce the error thoughts in our collective consciousness. Only by being a good student will we pass the final test of a passage through *"no-time"* or the test of a cold winter. We will grow again in the spring if we can create the seed of who we really are (a seed that can survive the *"no-time"* passage) It will then live long in the garden. What is this seed? Surely, it must be made of what we are, what we really are, not what some perceive we are, here in the third dimension.

What is a seed but a pattern, a gene pool, a series of yes and no switches in the software of life's human DNA? A seed also holds life's energy force. The seeds that we are aware of have stored energy—the bean, the acorn, wheat—they all have the "germ" or DNA or software. Also, they have the starch, the food to carry the life force through the winter and to re-establish it in the spring. That energy can be thought of as the emotional love of God.

What can be done for mankind to learn to survive the *human winter*? This is the question of humanity. What can be learned? I am sure we must understand the questions in the test. We can only pass the test if we know the universal truths. Error thoughts of the ego will surely cause us to fail. As in the lesson of the Titanic, ego worship assures failure. What then do we do? If we must learn to correct ego, we must learn to open to spirit and the truth of Spirit and the universe.

Mr. "B" teaches that in order to survive "*no-time,*" we must learn and prepare spiritually, mentally, and physically. Therefore, I must believe that what this book must do is to prepare us physically, mentally or spiritually for the final exam.

Our awareness of the third dimensional physical rules is available to us. These rules are printed in the physical history of the planet. To review a few of these rules, I might cite, the cycles of the glaciers, the physical evidence of the past catastrophes, the physical evidence of a humanity before the last catastrophe, the apparent lost knowledge and the carried over knowledge. If we know the universal truths of the third dimension, then we have a better chance of interpreting these physical signs and evidence. Also, if we know who we are as the co-creator of this dimension, then we have a chance of learning how we can become spiritually prepared. Remember the challenge is this:

"No-time," no magnetic field: **The creator/gardener may have the solar system pass through *No-time* in the not too distant future. I have named this *"the winter of humanity."* It will be a time when humanity is in suspended animation much as plants are in the winter.**

In the spring, some plants, if they survive the winter, are still plants; others are just tubers or roots and others are only seeds. These differences exist because of the software of each plant, the process it has devised to survive the killing frosts of winter. We too, are going to be asked to devise a way to survive this *human-winter*. We have done this before as modern man probably only about four times. Each final exam creates many changes in the being we know as humanity. Weak and poorly informed individuals would find it very difficult to survive these times. They will see themselves as victims instead of co- creators, and they will be unable to adjust their reality to make it survivable.

Others will know they are responsible intellectually, but will be unable to believe within their emotional bodies. These emotional bodies are necessary to insure the change to a new reality. As the propellant to change, the emotions of trust, faith, and love are essential.

Hopefully, some will understand their role in the final exam of this age. They will know they are co-creators of the test we will call the *"human-winter."* They will take the challenge to study and to become informed, to prepare both mentally and physically for the test.

The ancestors of the Algonquin and many other native groups have a knowledge that many of us lack. We could call it knowledge of the "time machine." The stone chambers of New England and the Kiva of the Southwest all were and are time machines for awareness. Just now we are beginning to discover that these time machines functioned with magnetic properties or sound properties. I am not yet prepared to say how these properties worked, only that they did and do work.

If in these time machines our reality awareness is not bound so tightly to our physically created reality, it may be free to travel to other aspects of time readily available all around us. The awareness may be able to perceive the energies we see as past or future, but always within the constraints of what the thoughts of the now are. In that way, we can examine the thoughts of the now and see what past they came out of and what possible future they will move into.

Mr. "B" has always said that we must give thanks to the universe for the experiences of the past, regardless of how we perceive them; for they, both positive and negative, have brought us to where we are today. These thoughts we hold today will generate a predicted future. It is for this reason that Mr. "B" says, "the ever-changing energies of today." He is reminding us that as we change our thoughts, our future changes, as do our perceptions of the past. Our reality today is, of course, based on our perception of the universal energies around us.

In the *No-time* test, one man may put his body in a safe place and then go forward into time to see if it was a safe place. If it appears that it is not, he may put it in another safer place and check his thoughts to test it. So, if a person's awareness is such that he can successfully accept the guidance when it comes, he may survive the "*human-winter*." If he or she cannot perceive the universe in its true form with its true realities, they may be unable to predict what will be safe or even accept that the test will come. If they hold fear, it will mean they do not trust that they can create their universe. Even if they believe the test is coming, they will draw danger to themselves with their fear.

The spirit that owns its own creations and can see humanity as "one," knows the test is not to survive the "*human-winter*" as an individual, but that humanity (the one) survives to live another season in the Master's garden. The individual, that hold the loving flowers and the fertile seeds will survive. Through them, the best will survive because that is why the human spirit created the test originally. That is why we do not fear the human winter that is to come, but welcome it as a chance to go within and cull the error thoughts of our current creations. Lovingly and without fear, we must create a seed that will survive as our brothers in the plant world. They do not fear winter. It just is. They adjust. We must also adjust if we are to survive.

Of course, the final exam of this age must be given. It is a challenge to the students on this orb we call Earth, but not a challenge to survive as an individual, but to be an agent to do a divine task in this third dimension. The gardener needs beings in his garden that respect his entire creations.

This book then is a manual on how to become a beautiful flower grown season after season in the garden of our creator. To do this, we must understand the garden; we must understand ourselves, our own energies; we must understand the other energies in the garden. Then we must, and this is the most important of all, harmonize all that we understand together—our being, the beings around us and the garden in which we wish to live. If we do this, "we (mankind) will dwell long upon this Earth."

I wish to close with this one thought. When we pass into the *no-time* or galactic wave, we will not be aware. As our Bible says, it will come as one in the night. We have no reason to fear; none should be concerned. If we are chosen to make a new reality in a changed world or if we cross the veil into our soul awareness, our loved ones and we will feel no pain. I have no time frame or magic beans with which to climb to another dimension. But we can prepare. To learn to love as Christ did will make either passage easier. It will also make the time now more beautiful. It is in my attempt to express this love that I have written this book. I wish for each of you a pleasant journey. The End.

Post Script: Why? Why Me? Why Us?

In the book called *Conversations With God*, Mr. Walsch asked God if Life was a school. God said *"No. ... The soul—your soul—knows all there is to know all the time."* It was more a problem of remembering and experiencing. He then goes on to explain it this way.

> *"In the beginning, that which Is is all there was, and there was nothing else. Yet All That Is could not know itself—because All That Is is all there was, and there was nothing else. And so, All That Is . . . was not. For in the absence of something else, All That Is, is not."*

> *"This is the great Is/Not Is to which mystics have referred from the beginning of time."* (20) p - 21, 22.

This sounds like double-talk. But if you think of the (All—That—Is) as the creator and his creation and the great (All—That—Is/Not) as some part of the creation, then it makes sense. One way to paraphrase it might be to say, God in His/Her majestic totality could not experience Itself. Therefore He/She created duality or the (All—That—Is/Not). From the reference point of the (All—That—Is/Not), us, the true majestic nature of God could be experienced. Hence, the meaning of our struggle to remember and experience.

In 1974 I had a dream in which words were running through my mind--hot/cold dark/light tall/short good/bad, etc. I was aware these words represented duality or scales of perception, but I was unaware of the greater context. Today I can better see the meaning. When the creator (as in all creation stories) took the void (darkness) and created light (the duality) he began the process of awareness. From that point on, the creator could begin to know the Him/Herself. We are all deeply involved in this creation. We struggle daily to define ourselves on these scales, always searching for the ultimate definition, the magnificence of God.

As I pondered this, on this beautiful morning, I remembered a story from 1960 when I was still in the Navy. I used to work with naval aircraft. We had a strong old propeller fighter called the AD - 5 Skyraider. It was a single engine plane with the engine and prop on the nose. It was left over from the Korean War. There were still a lot of squadrons being used on the smaller aircraft carriers.

One particular day I was walking across the ramp on which the planes were parked when I was stopped up short. I was looking at an AD - 5 that could have come right out of a comic book. About two feet of propeller was bent back on each of the four blades. They were almost at a perfect 90-degree angle. The left wing was also damaged on the end. Curious, I walked into the hanger to get the story. To my amazement the plane had flown in from the ocean in that condition.

Due to a mess-up when trying to land on the carrier, the plane had been flown directly into the deck planks. With a cool and no doubt skillful pilot, somehow it stayed in the air as it cleared the ship. The pilot then chose to fly it to the base where I saw it.

Until that day I knew this plane only by reputation, but on that day I experienced its truly rugged reality. Battered and tested, this plane and pilot had a defining moment. You can bet this pilot loved this plane. It never let him down but survived the challenge.

I believe this is how the creator looks at us, each of us, that has fought the battle of life, lead the charge, damaged in the fray, because through us, the great (All—That—Is/Not), the creator can experience him/her self. He must love us dearly and want us also to know and experience the true majesty of the (All—That—Is).

Why have I put this little story in this book? Well the challenges may be great in the coming *human winter*, but as the dependable little fighter plane, we to can rise to the challenge. In rising to this challenge, we will create a defining moment in the human story (his-tory). Some of us will sit on a mountaintop after the changes and thank the sun and it's creator for the new day. And the creator will look down on this new world that mankind has helped to create and continue to love us greatly.

There is a little more from this book that needs to be noted here. Walsch asks,

"Why is the world in the shape it is in?" ... God says, *"Your question infers that I choose these events, that it is My will and desire they should occur. Yet I do not will these things into being, I merely observe you doing so. And I do nothing to stop them, because to do so would be to thwart your will. That, in turn, would deprive you of the God experience, which is the experience you and I have chosen together."* (20) P - 29, 32

"The world's natural calamities and disasters—its tornados and hurricanes, volcanoes and floods—its physical turmoil's—are not created by you specifically. What is created by you is the degree to which these events touch your life."

"Events occur in the universe which no stretch of the imagination could claim you instigated or created."

"These events are created by the combined consciousness of man. All of the world, co-creating together, produces these experiences. What each of you do, individually, is move through them, deciding what, if anything, they mean to you, and who and what you are in relationship to them." (20) p -37.

These quotes, I think, help take some of the weight of negative creations from us individually. It doesn't mean we are victims, because we are not. It just means we did not create these challenges all by ourselves. In the process of working through them we become aware of the God-Experience.

As a scientist I know we must act quickly, not because of a vision or conversation with God, but because in the species record of the Earth it is already written. The human population curve now stands almost vertical. This means man, as a species will shortly damage his habitat to the extent a great collapse will follow. This would happen with or without the Galactic wave. It's a well-understood scientific law.

A Galactic Wave in the mind-body of God may well be necessary to preserve other elements of this great experiencing place called Earth. I believe, in reality, it would be preferable to allowing us to totally outstrip and pollute our environment. As God says, *"we are creating this future."* I suppose, in a way, it must be one or the other if we do not change the rules.

It is possible, however, to reach the threshold of love instead of fear. If this were achieved, an unconditional love so great would be created. It would be so powerful it would be available to all. I believe we can do this. That is also why I have written this book, as my part. What is your part? What personal demon must you concur? What spiritual task have you been assigned? Look into your soul and find the answers, so we as mankind, will survive and grow in this Garden of Eden we call Earth. For me, the book goes on. For you it ends here.

Conversations

R: "The second part (this book) right now I've put aside. When I get done with this case study (*Ancient Mines...*) I want to work on *Riding The Wild Orb* again. I think that should be done first." ***B: "Yes, we agree."*** R: "I had XXXX and XXXX both read this and it seamed like they had trouble believing it. Is this going to be my biggest problem?" ***B: "Without a basis in the sciences it's going to be somewhat difficult, but are you familiar with the hundredth monkey syndrome. That's what's going to occur. As it becomes more prevalent in the consciousness of more people, more people are going to accept it."***
***

R: "Ok, What should I pay the most attention to?" ***B: "The primary thought processes that should be utilized is the up-coming Earth changes—How to utilize these changes instead of being devastated by them. And how to prepare for the inevitable without creating fear or panic or anxiety."***
***

R: "Please describe the ceremonies in the stone chambers of New England and New Grange?" ***B: "They are both ceremonies that cleanse. But it cleanses beyond the toxins of the physical being, and it can transport one forward or backwards in time. If you have read much about the Kiva, the Kiva is the window in Native American where one time-walks and the same principle applies."***

R: "How about the dream I had some years ago where I had *not told* someone of the Earth changes?" **B: "Yes, but that's why you are compiling information. Your book has an important role to play. Thus, your contribution."**
***

R: "And this may be what is going to happen?" **B: "Indeed. When the polar axis shifts, it disturbs all things on this planet but primarily the weather patterns. Now this is being exemplified in a very small way by what is commonly called and laughingly referred to us, the El Nino. You can see very graphically how a slight shift in weather patterns can wreak havoc and devastation, or you can imagine if that is magnified by 360, what devastation can occur. And that is what occurs when the pole of your planet shifts."**
***

R: "What causes it to go back?" **B: "The same thing that caused it to shift. It is a magnetic fluctuation that is part of the galactic magnetic fields."**

"In that non-time. Because when you slice through or push through or however you - whatever time you - there is going to be a period of time, or a period, where time as you understand it to be does not exist" (long pause). **"I see I have created great confusion."** R: (laugh).

R: "Are astronomers aware of the Galactic Wave?"
B: "Some are but very few, they misinterpret it."

R: "That's fine, but do they have a name for it?" **B: "Well."** R: "Are they seeing something out there, that they have named, that is this Galactic Wave? That's what my question is." **B: "Yes, and various groups have various names for it. But there is a universal . . . it has to do with the theory of a black hole in space, which is not truly what this is."** R: "But it is connected to that?" **B: "Indeed, yes."** R: "It would react probable like that?" **B: "It would exactly."** R: "Because there would be no way for the light to get past it, I suppose. Are we already feeling the effects of this?" **B: "Yes, we are."**

R: "When you said the Galactic Wave would look and act like a black hole, did you mean they were different, but similar, or are they black holes?" **B: "It's not a black hole but it would act like one."** R: "OK."
***

R: "Gregg Braden talks about the lowering magnetic field and the increasing frequency. Is this a relation-ship and could you explain that some?" **B: "Yes, there is a relationship and its quite simple if you think about it. If this Galactic Wave is moving closer, what would naturally occur? (Long pause)** R: "You got me there!" **B: "Well, let me see, how can I explain this? In water for things to shift, and** *the poles and all of this we are conversant in, wouldn't it be rational thinking as the Galactic Wave approaches all of the things that affect your planet and your, umm,"* . . . R: "Galaxy" . . . *B: "Yes. Wouldn't it be logically deduced that it would affect the magnetics and alter them?"* R: "So they're all tied together in a sense." *B: "Oh, indeed."* R: "I don't totally understand, but I probably don't have the ability to understand." *B: "Oh, certainly you do."* R: (Laughing) "Well, I'll try."

R: "Is that affecting our temperature (now) then?" *B: "Yes."* R: "Is the magnetic field going down?" *B: "Slowly."*

R: "Is the photon belt we are passing through thickening, and if so, is it being caused by the pressing of the two belts?" *B: "Yes."* R: "It is thickening?" *B: "It is."* R: "And it is caused by the two belts already bumping together?" *B: "Yes."*
***
R: "So then we have a very yin time coming up (implied 5/5/2000)." *B: "Indeed . . . we . . . do. And we are including this universal "we" in that."* R: "Is that a time when things are going to happen?" *B: "There will be things occurring, but not catastrophic or cataclysmic at this time . . . yet."*

R: "You had told me I should pay attention to meteorite showers." *B: "Yes."* R: " . . . and November 17 and 18, 1998." *B: "Yes, you are absolutely correct."* R: "OK, you also said I should pay attention to the planet having the most effect, and Saturn was that planet. Is that true?" *B: "That is correct."* R: "And the dream I had, where the old car was being pulled apart, was that it too?" *B: "Yes."* R: "OK, and then the last part, the native Indian one (a comet, Temple-Tuttle, described by the Dakota Sioux, 11/12/1833). Is that the same one?" *B: "Yes."* R: "Then that date I came up with, November 19 and 20, 2031," *B: "Yes"* (Implied it was correct).R: "Is there actually going to be pieces of that comet hitting the Earth or is it just a sign?" *B: "We perceive it is just a sign."* R: "A sign. We should be getting closer to the Galactic Wave by that time?" *B: "Yes."*

R: (Later) "On November 17 and 18, 2031, we are going to get a sign from the comet Temple Tuttle." *B: "Yes."* R: "Will that be like normal shooting stars, or will there be a lot of pieces big enough to go all the way to the ground?" *B: "There will be sizable pieces that will reach the surface of your planet."* R: "When they come all the way down they make a big mark in the sky. They will be more impressive." *B: "Yes."* R: "It seems like it must have happened when the natives wrote about it?" *B: "Yes, when the stars fell, they state."*

R: "Is there someone in this area I should work with on this second book?" *B: "Of course, we are going to assist you, you know this, umm, as far as another individual, no."* R: "OK."

***

R: "I asked the question once how human DNA is related to the 64 parts of the I-Ching. I did not get the relationship correct." *B: "Why did you not?"* R: "I had said something to the effect, was it a relationship. Was it like a blending, when the baby was first born . . . was it setting up a relationship, or was it something that went on the entire life? You said it was more like it went on through the entire life, but can you explain that a little?" *B: "Well it begins, how do I explain? It follows the energy, the life force energy. Do you understand?"* R: "The solar system follows like an energy pattern." *B: "Yes."* R: "It's a moving pattern?" *B: "Yes."* R: "And we follow that same pattern then?" *B: "We do. Not as grand of scale, but certainly."* R: "So that's how they connect." (My idea of how it worked, added later). We would recognize certain energies and follow those more? *B: "It's like . . . how do you? These new grand babies. They have a part of a great many people encoded in their being. So they are a micro cosmic of all of those ancestral beings. Do you understand?"* R: "Yes, I think so. It's like a hologram. It's a piece, but not the whole, but a piece that reflects the whole." *B: "That is correct."*

R: "In a follow-up question, I was talking about the DNA switches and I was going to extrapolate but I failed to do so. You said, "yes, there is a universal energy that acts as human emotion," (in this example). Can you tell me about this energy?" *B: "Let's see if I can, . . . umm." (Long pause). "I can't think of a very good way to break it down so that it makes . . ."* R: it's not something I can understand that's OK." *B: "Well, it is so cosmic, it's not even . . ."* R: "Is it like thought energy though?" *B: "It is like thought energy, but it is . . . It has a higher electrical frequency then mere thought."* R: "OK, you are at a level where there is nothing I can experience it with." *B: "There is nothing, I can conjure to relate to it."*
***

R: "When the pole shifts does happen in *no-time*? Is what happens, that the ridged magnetic Earth crust moves like an electronic solenoid, back into a more harmonic magnetic?" (Implied alignment) *B: "Yes. Actually it would be this way, depending on where you are standing, I suppose."* (With a turning movement of the hands.) R: "This will create a pivot axis through the Earth." *B: "It has to."* R: "With one end in Africa if I have it correct." *B: "That's correct."* R: "And is this why there is so much species diversity in that part?" *B: "Yes."* R: "Because they don't get wiped out every few thousand years?" *B: "That is correct."*

R: "And will the Earth's crust try to turn and the water resists causing large tidal waves?" *B: "Yes, to the degree that it could be like a tsunami."* R: "Yes, and how far inland could they go?" *B: "That is not determined, but it is quite a ways inland. And don't let's forget about the lakes."* R: "Yes, any kind of water." *B: "Yes."* R: "The large lakes especially could do that. I was trying to get a handle on where the forces would be applied. You know if the force applied to the ridged crust and both the air and the water would be able to move."
***

R: "This probably won't be relevant either, but you said one time there would be extreme winds during the pole change period." *B: "Oh yes . . . umm."* R: "But we probably won't be aware of them?" *B: "You will not be aware of them."*
***

R: "What would be the speed of the winds here in this part of North America?" *B: "It could be very, very high."* R: "Like 200 miles per hour?" *B: "Maybe not quite that high, but somewhat approaching hurricane velocity."* R: "OK."

??

Bibliography

1 - Jeffrey Goodman, PhD *We Are the Earth Quake Generation*, Berkley Publishing Corporation, 1979 (General Ref.)

2 - Richard W. Noone, *5/5/2000, Ice, The Ultimate Disaster*, Harmony Books, NY, NY 1986 (General Reference)

3 - Lori Adaile Toye, *New World Atlas* (General Reference)

4 - Michael B. McElroy. *Planet Earth, Problems and Prospectus*, Edited by, Leith, Price, & Spencer

5 - John White, *Pole Shift*, A.R.E. Press, Virginia Beach, Virginia, 1987

6 - Peter D. Ward, *The Call of Distant Mammals*, Copernicus Springer—Verlag New York Inc. NY, NY, 1997

7 - Anthony F. Avendi, *"Archaeoastronomy in Pre-Columbian America"*, University of Texas, Austin, TX (General Ref.)

8 - Martin Palmer, Translation, *I-Ching, The Shamanic Oracle of Changes*, Thorsons, Harper Collins Publishers, 1995

9 - Science News, 2 February, 1974, *"Suggested That's The Earth's Magnetic Field Influence Atmospheric Pressure in The Upper Atmosphere and The Pressure System, Seamed to Move westward With The Magnetic Drift"* (5) - P -10. (General Ref.)

10 - J.F. Adkins, E.A. Boyle, L. Keiqwin & E. Cortijo; *"Variability of the North Atlantic Thermocline (SP) Circulation During The Last Interglacial Period,"* Nature 13 November 1997, p -154-156 (General Reference)

11 - K.A. Huahen, J. T. Overpeck, S.J. Lehman, M. Kashgarian, J. Southon, L.C. Peterson, R. Alley & D.M. Sigman; "*DeGlacial Changes in Ocean Circulation From Extended Radio Carbon Calibration,*" Nature, 1/1/98, P - 65-68

12 - Graham Hancock, *Finger Prints of The Gods*, Crown Trade Paperbacks, New York, NY, 1995

13 - Jose' Arguelles, *The Mayan Factor*, Bear & Company, Santa Fe, New Mexico, 1987

14 - Greg Braden, *Awakening to Zero Point, The Collective Initiation.* Radio Book Store Press, Bellevue, Washington, USA, 1997 (Including the Video Tape of the same name)

15 - Barbara Brennan, *Hands Of Light*, Bantam Books, New York N.Y. USA, 1988

16 - Machaelle Small Wright, *Behaving as if the God in All Life Mattered*, Perelandra, Ltd. Warrenton, VA. USA. 1997

17 - Steven J. Pyne, *Fire in America*, Princeton University Press, Princeton, New Jersey, 1982

18 - Tony Shearer, *Lord of the dawn*, Naturecraft, Healdsburg, CA. 1971

19 - Mark Bucahanan, *Beyond Reality*, New Scientist, March 14, 1998 (General Reference)

20 - Neale Donald Walsch, *Conversations with God*, G. P. Putnam's Sons, New York, NY, 1996

21 - Mayewski et al., Science, 1993-1994 The Greenland summit Ice Cores CD-ROM A modified version on, ARCSS/GISP2 Ice Core. 1/9/99

22 - Lawrence Blair, *Rhythms of Vision*, Warner Books Inc., NY, NY, 1975

23 - Toivo Jaakkola, Red-shift work on Internet. (General Ref.)

24 - Gilgamesh reference lost, my apologies to the reader.

25 - Giorgio De Santillana & Hertha Von Dechend, *Hamlets Mill*, David R. Godine, Boston, MA, Published 1977

26 - Ruffner & Blair, *Weather of US Cities, Third Edition*, Published 1987, p-230

27 - NOAA & NREL CD Rom: Solar Meteorological Surface Observation Network, 1961 - 1990, Sept. 1993. (General Ref.)

28 - William L. Donn, The Earth: Our Physical Environment, John Wiley & Sons, Inc., NY, NY (P-314)

29 - Rhodes W. Fairbridge and John E. Sanders, *The Suns Orbit AD750 - 2050, Basis for New Perspectives on Planetary Dynamics and Earth-Moon linkage.*

30 - Therdor Landscheidt, *Long-Range Forecasts of Solar Cycles and Climate Changes*, A paper for, Schroeter Institute for Research in Cycles of Solar Activity, F.R. Germany.

31 - Jean-Pierre Desmoulins, *Sunspot Cycles, are they Caused by Venus, Earth, and Jupiter Syzygies?* France. (Off Internet)

32 - Leon E. Stover and Bruce Kraig, *Stoneheng; The Indo-European Heritage*, Nelson - Hall, Chicago, Ill. 1979, p - 82

33 - Mystery of the Sphinx, (Vido Tape) NBC - TV, 1993